RAJIV GANDHI

The Author with Shri Rajiv Gandhi in June 1990.

RAJIV GANDHI
His Vision of the 21st Century
Science, Technology and National Development

DR. PAWAN SIKKA

KALPAZ PUBLICATIONS
DELHI-110052

Rajiv Gandhi : His Vision of the 21st Century-Science, Technology and National Development

Rs. 750

ISBN: 81-7835-559-0

Published in 2007 in India by
Kalpaz Publications
C-30, Satyawati Nagar,
Delhi-110052
Phone: 9212729499
E-mail: kalpaz@hotmail.com

Lassertype Setting by: Rudra Computer Graphics, Delhi
Printed at: Salasar Imaging System, Delhi

Dedicated to My Parents

Shrimati Shakuntla Devi
and
Shri Guranditta Mal Sikka

Contents

...To take India ahead, we have to look towards the optimum utilization of our resources. Our biggest resource is the human resource. And we shall develop it and also develop our natural resources and we will utilize our industrial and capital resources to the best benefit.

" To do this, we need technology. We need a new education and we need to look after the health of our people so that they are up to the task. But most of all, it will need managerial skill and it will need political will and we will give you both.

- Rajiv Gandhi
Lok Sabha, 22 January 1985

Preface

Rajiv Gandhi was neither a scientist nor a politician in the conventional sense. He was a self-confident person with a scientific bent of mind and a zeal for moving ahead. He realized that modern science and technology can play a useful role in social uplift, in creating a more open society and in bringing India closer together. He saw society with a new approach. His was an innovative mind, attempting to redefine India's role in a changing global environment. He had a modern vision for India. He had a vision of building a strong and vibrant India with the inputs of science and technology. He was the creator of the vibrant force of change and was the harbinger of the generational change, not just in Indian politics, but in almost all spheres of national life. As a human being, he combined the grace of Englishman with the concern of helping the weaker sections of the society. He said that *we have to understand that science is not something esoteric, it is the common man's helper to assist and transform our lives.*

As a Prime Minister of India, in 1984 – 1989, Rajiv Gandhi brought with him dynamism, hope and new vision. He, like his grandfather Pandit Jawahar Lal Nehru and mother Mrs. Indira Gandhi, believed that science and technology held the key to India's future that could transform her into a modern state. He knew technology and took interest in it. He understood the role of technology in meeting the basic human needs. He gave a clarion call to the nation to take a quantum leap into the 21st century. He said, in his maiden speech in the Lok Sabha, on 22 January 1985, that – *in the coming years, we will build a united secular free India where a person's work is not measured by his cast, creed, region or religion. We will build an India which is dynamic, an India which can move ahead with the rest of the world.* He was a leader far ahead of his time.

I too have a dream – he said in the early years of his Prime Ministership. It was a dream of the architect of modern India, of using science and technology in the day-to-day life so that India could emerge as a progressive and technologically advanced nation. It was a dream of hope, of rebirth and re-commitment to the ideals of the nation that had undergone the baptism of fire through its long struggle from colonial rule. It was a dream of an India, peaceful yet strong which could take its rightful place in the community of nations. A dream of a strong, proud and united India, which would march into the 21st century, with courage and confidence. A dream which would help realise the fullest potential of India, of every Indian. It was his dream of modernizing India, of bringing her fully technologically, economically and socially into the new millennium. He felt: *We can achieve world leadership in key areas by refocusing our strategies on areas that we feel are more relevant or necessary to us, or areas that we want to go ahead in….*

This is not a political biography of Rajiv Gandhi, but an attempt to understand how a young and dynamic person with a modern and scientific outlook intended to provide technological solutions to the age-old problems afflicting the Indian society for long. This is, in fact, a scientific profile of a leader who was as much concerned with the technology of putting satellites in space, as much as, using modern technology to provide drinking water to every village in India, to immunize pregnant women and infants etc. He introduced computerization in India. He also had a great liking for nature and environment. He had taken up a mission to clean up the revered Ganges river and rid it of pollution. He gave the concept of technology missions that married his social concerns with his interests in modern technology. His a another major contribution was to give a new thrust to the prestige and stature of the country in the international arena. The contributions made by him towards reducing international friction and tensions were appreciated by political leaders the world over. His constructive participation benefited the United Nations, the Non-Aligned Movement and the Commonwealth Nations. At the Ninth Summit of the Non-Aligned Movement, he proposed the institution of a Planet Protection Fund for providing latest conservation technologies to the developing countries towards the protection of the global environment. The Rajiv era brought in many new ideas. All of them could not be implemented, in a short period of five years, yet they gave a new course to the history of modern India. One could compile a systematic and exhaustive list of everything that he did and the things begun and left undone. But this would not give us the measure of the man and his mission. We would lose the wood for the trees of his Prime Ministership.

However, this is also not the story of his rise to fame or the tragedy that followed. It is just a faithful account of what happened in the field of science and technology during his dynamic period of Prime Ministership. Rajiv Gandhi, in the ultimate analysis, in the light of his own words, drawn from the material available to me, *believed in the growth of the individual as well as of the nation.* At the inaugural ceremony of the Indira Gandhi National Open University, he said, on 18 December 1985 that – *We have recently clubbed together certain ministries and labeled them* ***"Human Resources Development"*** *not because we wanted to give a fancy paint job but because what we really want is to develop the human resources. What we must do is to turn this (population) problem into the biggest asset and that will happen if we are able to develop the human resources in our country and this is what we must attempt to do; develop them not just in teaching them technology, teaching them sciences or medicine or whatever...but also develop a sense of value and idealism, a commitment to the country.*

There is no doubt that he was a man in a hurry. He wanted to do things fast. This trait was reflected in all the facets of his character and in each sphere of the work. Women's education, plight of women and children, spread of literacy, use of modern took up with missionary zeal. He could see that there was a strong nexus between science and technology and economic development of the society for the emergence of modern India.

This is a companion volume to my earlier book, Rajiv Gandhi-selected speeches on science and technology, providing his major observations on the current state of affairs in the field of science and technology. This book contains an in-depth study of the writings and speeches of Rajiv Gandhi, delivered on science and technology, during his active years at various national and international fora. They show his mind and ideology, as well as, his frankness and sincere zeal for the effective utilization of science and technology towards the welfare of mankind. They provide new directions to the application of science and technology for the techno-economic development of India of the 21st century. He cultivated the spirit of discovering something new . He was a crusader of modern science and technology and elucidated his inspiring vision in clear and confident terms, often contradicting the dominant discourse of his time. It was his vision of making India progressed, as closed as possible, to the world in all spheres of human activity. He evolved as an individual voice. This book belongs to him, not me as you can hear his voice in it. He had a vision for a modern India and had an important role to play in its fulfillment. He said in the Rajya Sabha on 23 January 1985 : *The challenges before our country are many. We have to modernize India. We have to change the thinking of the people of India to look ahead into the future and not to keep on dwelling on the past. We have to make India self-reliant in every important sphere. We have to create a dynamic country that is equal to any other country in the world.*

India surged ahead with Rajiv Gandhi. He accelerated the pace of change towards liberalization and brought about new attitudinal changes in the government and people. He was instrumental in fostering an atmosphere of modernity in the country. His clear vision navigated India towards progress and prosperity. His slogan *Mera Bharat Mahan* (my India is great) was actually aimed at keeping the country together.

His untimely and unnatural death at the age of 47, in 1991, cut-short his dream of building a modern, strong and technologically advanced India of the 21st century. He will be remembered for his vision and pioneering efforts of navigating India into the new millennium with the application of science and technology. His absence will be keenly felt but his vision of an economically vibrant India will endure. He lived a short life long. He was in the genre of those great men produced by our country, who shone briefly on the firmament, but left a brilliance that will continue for years thereafter. He was Prime Minister of India for five years only, yet his half - decade seems to have left an imprint, which bespeaks a much longer tenure. In his passing away we have not lost a person, but a direction for the future of science and technology in India. He was –

A man
Whose thought changed lives,
dreams set standards, and
presence made a difference
to the world.

It is hoped that the inspiring vision of Rajiv Gandhi, of modernising India with the current developments of science and technology, if implemented in letter and spirit, would go a long way in benefiting the society. He suggested many reforms in science policy related issues concerning the science and society. The revival of India's glory was meant to give a definite direction to every Indian for contributing his might towards this end. If the government has the gumption to go through these reforms it will transform the outlook for the Indian youth and release the country's potential to become an economic power. His vision continues to light up the entire nation even today – showing the path, and leading the way. Our scientific manpower, so impressive in number and quality, will be of little service if it does not prepare us for the future and does not find answers to the inherited as well as new problems. India may be a brain bank to the world. But it does not help if other countries cash in on this more frequently than India itself. Now, it is upto the future generations to translate his vision into reality for making a new, vibrant and resurgent India of the 21st century.

I am grateful to: Nehru Memorial Museum and Library, New Delhi; Publications Division, Ministry of Information and Broadcasting, Government of India, New Delhi; Rajiv Gandhi Foundation, New Delhi; Indian Science Congress Association, Kolkata; India International Centre Library, New Delhi; British Broadcasting Corporation (BBC), London, U.K.; Viking Penguin Books India (P) Ltd., New Delhi UBS PD and many others as quoted in the text, for their permission and kindness to use their libraries, copyright texts etc. required in bringing out this book, whose idea was conceived by me way back in June 1991. It has taken in fact, more than 15 long years, for the various reasons, for the book to see light of the day.

I have to mention my family, my wife Dr. Shalini Sikka, and children Dr.Saurabh Sikka, Dr. Ayushi Sikka Chugh, Dr. Tarun Chugh and little master Vayun Chugh for their cooperation, patience and understanding. Finally, my sincere tribute to Rajiv Gandhi for providing me this great opportunity. I shall not be dealing now as a historian of Rajiv Gandhi, which I am not, but merely a physicist trying to understand his scientific outlook towards life and the people.

22 March 2007 **Dr. Pawan Sikka**
New Delhi

1

Rajiv Gandhi His Fascination for Science and Technology

I have nursed a dream, a dream of the great Indian people marching confidently into the future. I dream of an India that excels itself. Together we can fulfill that dream.

— ***Rajiv* Gandhi**

Rajivaratna Birjees Nehru Gandhi*, born on 20 August 1944, to Mrs. Indira Gandhi and Mr. Firoz Gandhi, in Mumbai, had his early education at Doon School, Dehradun and passed his Cambridge entrance examination in London, in August 1962. He studied Mechanical Engineering at Trinity College, Cambridge and Imperial College, London, England. But, later he took up flying as a profession with the Indian Airlines. His job as a pilot spurred his interest in the new and emerging areas of electronics and telecommunications.

Rajiv Gandhi had a scientific bent of mind. He was a great dabbler in many things. A deft motor mechanic, he at the least indication would be below his car to mend it, an expert cameraman. Even as a pilot, he was always at one or the other manual errand.

---

* His name as recorded in his baby book and school records.

In 1974, he assembled his ham radio set from a do-it-yourself kit and became an amateur radio operator. He had a passion for conservation and environmental studies, classical and western music (Mozart), target shooting, outdoor life and the need to preserve Indian culture. His bookshelves were stacked with books on science and engineering.

He entered the public life on 10 May 1981 and became a member of the Seventh Lok Sabha (Parliament) on 17the August 1981. Rajiv Gandhi came to politics and to the Parliament as a fresh breze. In his maiden speech in the Lok Sabha on 11 March 1982, he said; as Sood puts it – "The issues Rajiv Gandhi raised and the manner in which it was dealt with reflected on inherent pragmatism. Not for him, this soaring political rhetoric which echoes all too briefly in the Lok Sabha to leaving faint memory, not for him populist slogan aimed at cheap popularity, Mr. Gandhi chose to dwell upon such seemingly mundane, but nationally important issues as improving capacity utilization and keeping up the momentum of production. He pointed out with irrefutable logic that capacity utilization in power generation was woefully low at 46 percent. *He made the significant point that coal production should be measured in calorific value rather than in tonnage.* He suggested improvement of infrastructure to utilize the irrigation potential of the country better. He also called for more funds for research in renewable sources of energy, a programme that is vitally needed eminently possible in India with a plethora of resources and almost year-round sunlight.
He was an engineer-with-a-vision."[2]

All these years Rajiv had shown avid interest in electronics. He was mainly responsible for the decision in mid-1983 to do an about-turn on electronics policy, to reduce excise and custom duties and expand the market for consumer electronic items, notably for T.V. When a public sector officer suggested to him that low powered transmitters could very quickly and cheaply expand the total T.V. network, the idea was immediately accepted and pushed through with enhanced budget.[3]

Once a reluctant entrant to politics, he was a politician in the embryo – with his lineage that stretches from his maternal grandfather, Pandit Jawaharlal Nehru to his own parents – all seasoned politicians of international level. Politics was in his genes. He probably imbibed the intricacies of political contours and social upliftment, with his breakfast cereals. He had an upbringing in an atmosphere in which politics and scientific outlook on life were inevitably had a strong ambience. He was appointed Prime Minister of India at the young age of 40 years, following the assassination of his mother, Mrs Indira Gandhi, on 31 October 1984. He came like a whiff of the fresh air. His entry into the politics, therefore made an immediate impact and changed the entire political scenario in India. He grew up at the track and understood the magnitude of the most critical and urgent problems that faced India. He studied and understood India's glorious past, was aware of the demands and compulsions of the present and was concerned about the future. He had one point agenda before him, that was of using science and technology for the socio-economic development of India.

Rajiv Gandhi had, soon after assuming the Prime Ministership of India, promised the nation, a Government that worked faster. He also declared that he wanted to lead India, into the 21st century. In his first broadcast to the nation, on 12 November 1984, he said –

> *As we build today so will be the tomorrow. Together we will build for an India of the 21st century. Together we will transform what needs transformation. Together we will face challenges and obstacles to progress. Together we will create an India that is strong, wise and great – a flame of peace and tolerance.*

Rajiv Gandhi was the visionary leader who saw the critical role that science and technology would play in making India a leading nation of the world. He projected an image of modernity and infused a new confidence in the masses, which was marked by a vision largely technocratic and relying heavily on science and technology. Technology was passion with him. Technology not for the sake of technology, but in the service of basic developmental tasks. To him, technology was more than science. It was a practical tool to make the lives of ordinary people better. He dreamt India of the 21st century. He outlined his task ahead – *Our task today is to bring India to the threshold of the 21st century – free from the burden of poverty, legacy of our colonial past and capable of meeting the rising aspirations of our people. This will require sustained efforts on our part. How are we going to prepare the nation to meet the challenges of the next century, to meet the challenges of the latest technology, as it comes? ... Development has to mean absorption of the most modern techniques at the most basic levels in our society...*

In a broadcast to the nation, on 5 January 1985, he said – *It is a privilege to be born in India and to be heir to its great civilization .... From time to time, I shall share with you my ideas, my hopes, my struggles. But even more, I want to listen to you, to your difficulties, your ideas, your hopes. Together we shall share the burden and the ecstasy of building our India. ...Together we will build an India of the twenty-first century.*

Rajiv Gandhi observed that-

> ...India's freedom struggle was a saga of the resistance of an unarmed people against the world's biggest empire. On gaining freedom, we adopted a multi-party parliamentary system. The Indian nation is built on the principles of democracy, secularism and socialism. We have adopted the method of planned development and we have concentrated all our energies on overcoming mass poverty which was the legacy of two centuries of colonization. We have scored notable success. In grain production, we have become self-sufficient and are able to export cereals to others. A country, which had virtually no industry, has now become a major industrial nation. The work of our research laboratories in finding solutions to several deep-seated problems commands the respect of the international scientific community.

While enunciating his vision of modern India of 21st century, he (Rajiv Gandhi) had the guiding principles of his grandfather Pandit Jawaharlal Nehru before him, who said - *We have to build up this great country into a mighty nation, mighty not in the ordinary sense of the word, that is having great armies and all that, but mighty in thought, mighty in action, mighty in culture and mighty in its peaceful service of humanity.*[5] Rajiv Gandhi defined his vision, while addressing the Congress of the United States of America, on 12 June 1985, within a few months of his taking over as the Prime Minister of India. He said –

> *I have been elected Prime Minister of India at a time when our nation stands poised for a new surge of growth. Our leaders in the past thirty years have established firm foundations on which we have now to build. India is an old country but a young nation; and like the young everywhere we are impatient.*
>
> *... I am young, and I too have a dream ... I dream of an India – strong, independent, self-reliant and in the forefront, in the front rank of the nations of the world in the service of mankind. I am committed to realizing that dream through dedication, hard work and the collective determination of our people. We will welcome all the cooperation that we can get.*

He possessed an amazing power of imagination, further strengthened by his scientific temperament. He introduced youthful dynamism, scientific precision and a spirit of dedication in the Indian system of governance. He had an unflinching faith in science and technology to transform the lives of people and to meet their basic needs. Science and technology were the basis of Rajiv's concern with bringing India into the 21st century. He inspired scientists and encouraged innovation. But it concerned him that science and technology were confined to the laboratories, not making an impact on poverty.[6] He was for the true role of the scientist as an innovator rather than as a conservator.

Rajiv Gandhi had a great fascination for science and technology and its effective utilization for the social transformation. He projected modern scientific outlook and qualities then needed to speed up the process for achieving the techno-economic development of India. He inspired scientists and encouraged innovation. Science and Technology were the basis of Rajiv's concern with bringing India into the 21st century.

Pandit Nehru had said: It is science alone that can solve the problems of hunger and poverty, of insanitation and illiteracy, of superstition and vast resources running to waste, of a big country, inhabited by starving people. ***This is the prism which encompasses all our needs and aspirations*** – said Rajiv Gandhi at the 74th Session of the Indian Science Congress Association, held at Bangalore, on 3 January 1987. With his imaginative, innovative and modern approach, he initiated several new projects and programmes for harnessing the application of science and technology towards alleviating poverty and creating employment opportunities, as well as, for providing thereby good quality of life to the people. He saw tremendous potential of modern science and technology in the process of socio-economic development of India. He gave new directions and promoted several programmes in electronics, environment and forest conservation etc. He had in fact developed an immense interest in the technology relating to these fields . As an ardent visionary, he wanted to link-up scientific and technological developments with the industrial development and socio -economic growth of India.

The relationship between science and society for development appears to be weak in India. Scientific activities should accelerate the pace of social change in the country, he said, while inaugurating the Conference on Science and Technology in India – Retrospect and Prospect on 13 November 1985, in New Delhi. He further stressed the need for inculcating scientific temper among people enabling them to derive maximum benefits of the advancements taking place in all sectors of science and technology.

Development of Electronics

He was one of the very few politicians who recognised the importance of technological changes taking place in information sector and made us aware of its impact and prepared us for this massive development. His fresh approach on the economic and industrial fronts, breaking the dogmas, resulted in ushering of an **electronic era** in India, together with liberalization of the Industrial policy. His fascination with electronics and telecommunications resulted in revamping the antiquated telephone systems to meet the public demands. A National Informatics Centre, New Delhi, was set up then to store all the economic data of the country.

Agriculture:

Jawaharlal Nehru is acclaimed for his contribution to the industrialisation and modernisation of India. His understanding of and concern for rural problems has not received due recognition. It has even become fashionable to accuse him of neglecting agriculture. On the contrary, he steered Indian planning so that there would be no danger of industrialisation, hampering agriculture. He laid stress on irrigation, agricultural extension and research and other essential requirements of rural regeneration, such as land reform. Where he differed from the more orthodox school of rural thought was in his emphasis on science as the catalyst to visibly increase agricultural output and improve rural life. He looked to our scientists to find answers to the main problem of our villages and our country – poverty, said Mrs Indira Gandhi, on 3 January 1978.[7]

Realising that agriculture was the backbone of Indian economy, Rajiv Gandhi stressed upon the need for faster and even agricultural growth, say in Northeastern part of India, which required the extension of green revolution to other regions. During his brief tenure as Prime Minister of India, the production of food grains touched an all time high record in India. The scheme of setting up Krishi Vigyan Kendras in all districts of India was also then formulated for facilitating the transfer of high-tech and scientific knowledge to the farmers. Rajiv Gandhi said – There *is no dichotomy between agricultural development and national development. The former is the foundation of the later.*

Protection of the Environment

Rajiv Gandhi was deeply concerned about the problem of the environmental degradation and its catastrophic impact on human

human civilization. He said on 7 November 1985, that - *In a developing country, one has to balance, the costs and benefits of exploiting resources and protecting the environment, whether it is in terms of destruction of certain areas to put up industry or to put up mines or other development projects; whether it is in terms of pollution of rivers, of air or various areas. We must bear in mind that ultimately there is no short cut. If we do not pay a price today, we will invariably have to pay a much heavier price tomorrow. We must build this into our awareness.*

Besides the Department of Environment, the setting up of the Central Ganga Authority and the implementation of the Ganga Action Plan, to prevent the pollution of the river Ganga were the major events, which took place during his active years. He launched a grandiose project to clean the river Ganges. Also, he set up a National Wasteland Development Board for bringing five million hectares of land, every year, under the fuel-wood and fodder plantation. He introduced a mechanism of assessing the environmental impact of the developmental work, so as to harmonize development with environment.

Rajiv Gandhi had the wisdom of placing environment in the wider context of international cooperation, which must be pursued through international institutions. He was convinced that much of the blame for the depletion of the ozone layer, for global warming, for the dumping of hazardous waste and for deforestation must be laid at the door of the industrialised countries. The high levels of consumption and production by the industrialized countries not only strained available natural resources but also led to an alarming emission of pollutants into the atmosphere and thus the main responsibility and burden for combating pollution and environmental degradation must necessarily be theirs. He could well see the correlation between environmental protection and the general issue of development and thus believed that in any global endeavour, the legitimate concerns and interests of the developing countries must be fully met. Moreover, he emphasized the need of a global effort to bring within reach of all, developing and developed countries, the technologies that existed and that were yet to be developed, to combat pollution and environmental degradation. He called for a global effort to ensure access to environment-friendly technologies and the funding of research and development into such technologies. With these ends he proposed the establishment of a Planet Protection Fund (PPF), under the aegis of the United Nations to be used to protect the environment by developing or acquiring conservation-compatible technologies in critical areas which could then be brought into the public domain for the benefit of both developing and developed countries. The PPF, he believed, would become the fulcrum for a truly cooperative global endeavour to measure up to a problem of global dimensions and global implications. Thus, very often, he asserted that environmental issues were closely linked to the larger issues of peaceful co-existence, international cooperation, disarmament and development.

Technology Missions

"India has reached a stage of development in technology when it is no longer enough for us to draw up plans and then to seek the technological wherewithal to execute them. It is necessary, and it should be possible for our scientists and technologists to tell us what can be achieved and how it should be done... ...? Another urgent need is to make the fullest use of the available manpower, equipment and so on. Much of the money, which is now spent on research and design, is distributed to various laboratories. There is a feeling that the R & D effort is not contributing scientifically to economic growth and that scientists and technologists should concentrate on social gains and rapid economic development. Can we not select specific fields for group efforts rather than spreading our resources thinly over a wider area? Equipment and apparatus are now becoming more and more sophisticated and hence increasingly expensive. Our national laboratories are well equipped but others run by individual establishments and our universities are not always so. Is it not possible to evolve some way of sharing these facilities?" said Mrs. Indira Gandhi.[8]

Rajiv Gandhi understood the point: As a major initiative, he launched the concept of Technology Missions. The concept of these missions and the way they were implemented, deserve to be missions and the way they were implemented, deserve to be emphasized as a major technology management breakthrough. For instance, in solving the water problem, he was not only satisfied by only targeting the source but would delve with the intricacies of reaching the supply at the threshold. The mission-oriented approach was a model on how to create an organizational structure by involving many institutions, R & D labs etc. for the purpose, spelling out clear-cut goals, schedules and arranging finance for the whole exercise. A set of six technology missions was identified in the fields of literacy, drinking water, oilseeds, immunization and telecommunication to achieve excellence and modernization in the country.

His mission mode approach of the applications of science and technology to some of the crucial sectors of our economy strengthened the economy immensely. The nation will remember him for making India a global player in IT (information technology), computer software, production of liquid milk, natural rubber and cane sugar. These missions expressed his ambition to do something really big for the benefit of people by employing science and technology.

Industrial Development

Rajiv Gandhi gave a new orientation to the industrial development with the liberalization of the industrial policy in order to achieve a higher growth rate. He had a deep understanding in regard to the role of technology and industry and the place of modern management techniques in it. He stressed upon the improvement in productivity, absorption of modern technology, and a fuller utilization of the capacities and capabilities built over the years in the fields of science, technology and industry, towards the overall socio-economic development of India.

He gave a new fillip to the productive process to encourage quality and healthy competition. He believed in adopting an outward policy. For that the country must export more to pay for its imports and for this purpose the Indian products must be able to compete in the world market. The restructuring of the conventional trade, in the world market began during his dynamic years. He laid the foundation of a managerial revolution so that India successfully competes globally in the future.

Other Areas

The main reason for the (public) support (to science & technology), is the hope that science and technology can contribute to the betterment of the living conditions of our people, and to the solution of some of their basic everyday difficulties. Poverty and illiteracy, unemployment and mal-employment, urban- rural distances, social tensions arising out of parochial feelings based on religion or caste. These are the problems threatening our future...I do recognize that many of our problems are not amenable to scientific solution in the narrow sense of the term. At the same time, science and technology can create the atmosphere of confidence and creative endeavour, which can help us towards solutions – said Mrs. Indira Gandhi. [9]

Rajiv Gandhi gave priority to the use of non-conventional sources of energy, which led to the production of the solar cookers & heaters, solar lanterns, solar photovoltaic panels etc. in India. He also gave fillip to India's space and nuclear programmes for peace and prosperity. Besides, he promoted the development of missile-based defence technologies, recognizing their need for precision and accuracy. He was concerned for consolidating the strength of science in India. He felt although India has made striking advances in atomic energy, space exploration, agriculture and industrial production, yet inspite of the provisions of administrative and financial resources, India has not excelled in world science. He had novel technological ideas to build a vibrant, modern and technological India. At the same time, he knew that the real job of governance was to bring relief to the poor, both rural and urban India.

Whichever fields we choose to survey – education, health, industry, transport, communication – we find evidence of unprecedented change. The colonial stagnation has given way to a steady movement for

> *socio – economic transformation. This transformation is taking place through the application of science and technology. More than anything else, we need more peace in the world and peace in our region to complete the revolutionary tasks we have on our own hands,* said Rajiv Gandhi at the International Symposium on Science, Technology and Development, held in New Delhi on 25 March 1987.

"Development is being crippled because of the militarisation of the scientific endeavour in the world. ... we recognize that the non-violent world we seek is possible only if the international community including the scientific community, eschews the immortality of science for destruction and cooperatively adopts the ethos of science for creativity. We would like to see the Indian scientific community take the lead in this regard" – said Rajiv Gandhi at the 76th session of the Indian Science Congress Association, held at Madurai, on 3 January 1989.

High-Tech Areas

Rajiv Gandhi was very much impressed with India's performance in high-tech areas of science and technology, viz, Atomic energy, Launching of satellite, Testing of Ballistic missiles, Ocean exploration, including expeditions to Antarctica etc. He desired the use of these high-tech areas for the peaceful uses and expressed confidence in sharing knowledge in these fields with other developing countries for the welfare of humankind. He said while dedicating the fast breeder reactor to the nation, at Madras Atomic Power Project, Madras (now Chennai) on 16 December 1985 –

> *India is committed to the peaceful uses of atomic energy. Our conditions are such that we must exploit all our energy resources to the maximum to back up our development efforts. Our history and heritage of tolerance, of non-violence, more recently of non-alignment makes us, allows us, to use this energy positively for generating energy and we have seen*

that it allows us to use self-restraint and self-control and not use this energy for negative purposes.

International cooperation in science and technology, particularly in the field of space, can go a long way towards ensuring a better standard of life for all humankind. Many important activities such as the monitoring of the environment, meteorological phenomenon and ocean-atmospheric dynamics are global in nature. On the other hand, a large number of problems such as domestic communications, education, rural development and resource management require the application of space technology based on aspirations of the people of each developing country and their economic, cultural, social and technical background. We believe that much greater concerted international effort is required to enable developing countries to have full access to the benefits of space technology. On our part, having derived considerable benefits from international cooperation, we have regarded it as our moral obligation to initiate a new programme on a "Sharing of experiences in Space" called SHARES. Under this programme we have already trained a number of scientists from developing countries in areas of relevance to them. We reiterate our firm and unequivocal commitment to international cooperation in the peaceful exploration and utilization of outer space, for the development of humanity as a whole. If, as recognized by the United Nations, Space is to be treated as the "Common heritage of all mankind", its pristine tranquility must not be jeopardized by extending our quarrels on earth into space. Recent attempts to extend the introduction of destructive weapons into space, are ominous developments, of great concern to humanity. Every step taken with a view to creating impenetrable defences has only escalated the arms race and brought humankind that much closer to its end. More than ever today, human survival depends upon concerted action and immediate negotiations to usher in a world free of nuclear weapons and rooted in non-violence.

Rajiv Gandhi expressed the above sentiments at the 30th Congress of the International Astronomical Federation held at Bangalore on 10 October 1988. He was inspired by Pandit Nehru who said in 1944, that –

It can hardly be challenged, that in the context of the modern world, no country can be politically and economically independent, even within the framework of international inter-dependence, unless it is highly industrialized and developed its power resources to the utmost. Nor can it achieve or maintain high standard of living and liquidate poverty without the modern technology, in almost every sphere of life.[10]

Rajiv Gandhi stressed the need to develop a strong base of indigenous capability in science and technology while interacting with international community to keep abreast of the latest developments and assume a leadership role in the scientific field. The filtering of knowledge in the scientific and the technological advancements from abroad selectively, he believed, could bring prosperity to the nation as a whole. However he was certain that for our self-sufficiency, Indian science and technclogy needed to be given a major thrust. In this regard, as early as in December 1985, Rajiv Gandhi observed: *Unless we are able to give science and technology in India, not just imported science and technology, but Indian science and technology a major thrust, we will not be able to keep up this self-sufficiency that we have generated so far.*

While appreciating the achievements of India in the fields of space, agriculture, defence and nuclear fields, he said in the Lok Sabha (Parliament) on 10 April 1986, that –

We have shown that when India accepts a challenge, when our scientists, when our technologists accept a challenge, they need that challenge and they deliver

> *the goods. Today, we must give them the backing they need to achieve similar results in many other fields. Once more, we would like to show that India can do it and will do it. Where science and technology is concerned, we must keep in mind that nothing but the best will do for the country; and we must work towards that end. With everybody's support, I believe we will be able to do it.*

In his address to the 73rd Session of the Indian Science Congress Association, New Delhi on 7 January 1986, Rajiv Gandhi said – "Our scientists must concentrate on what is most meaningful for a country like India. In today's circumstances that means in the rural areas, the agricultural sector, and the various sectors that support our agricultural and rural industry. Our scientists have considerable achievements to their credit during these past years. They have put India in a strong, self-reliant position, not just in agriculture but also in certain strategic and sensitive areas where it was difficult for us to import technology. Where there have been real challenges, where the chips have been down, our scientists have risen to the occasion and have shown the world that they are second to none when it comes to capability, competence and achievement". While delivering his inaugural address at the 75th Session of Indian Science Congress Association, Pune on 7 January 1988 at , Rajiv Gandhi said –

> *... We must not be inhibited. We should boldly seize what is new, examine the opportunities and adopt what suits us. We should let the adventure of discovery and spirit of invention takes us forward to meet our goal. ... In this spirit we have to approach the new areas of science and technology that are opening up the world over. We cannot be left behind in such fields as biotechnology, super conductivity, faster computers, renewable energy sources, new composite materials and a host of other fields and products.*
>
> *... We must not only be in tune with research in these areas, we must know how they are being harnessed in*

in the service of society. Ultimately it is such a harnessing that compels attention and gives science its raison d'etre. The nation looks to its scientists to help policy makers to determine scientific, time- bound objectives in major areas of national endeavour. We must then bend all our energy to the achievement of such goals. That is the only road to self-reliance.

India has made striking advances in atomic energy, space research, agricultural and industrial production in the past four decades. Yet inspite of the provision of sufficient funds, good scientific infrastructure policies and promotional support of the Government, there were some lacunae. While infusing a new confidence, Rajiv Gandhi reminded the Indian scientific community at the Sir Shanti Swarup Bhatnagar Award giving ceremony on 17 October 1988 in New Delhi that–

We need to broaden the areas where we are really upfront, widen them and look at those areas in a more objective, perhaps, more aggressive way. We have to look at things in terms of what we want to make of India. I find that we have been having inward looking policies in development areas. We have to look at where we want to take the country, what are the challenges that the country will be facing, may be economic challenges, may be security challenges, other challenges – and what we need to do to strengthen ourselves to face these challenges ?

The challenges, of course, will depend on what we want to make of our country, where we want to take our country. Today, when international relations are changing very rapidly and very radically, we must take the opportunity to evaluate where India should be in the new scheme of things. If India is to take her due place in the world, then we need to work very aggressively at home to develop in those areas and fields, which are essential in the new scheme of things. This is where the role of our scientists, our

> *the role of our scientists, our technologists become very much more important than it has been in the past.*

In this context, he said at IIT, Delhi, that – *Perhaps the biggest challenge that we have today in science and technology is not in regard to the peaks that we produce. We have people who are equal to many in the world. We are happy that many have gone to the top of their fields. But this has not filtered down enough, amongst our people. We want not merely pillars of knowledge but pyramids of knowledge. This change has to be brought about.*

India cannot divorce science from the urgent needs of society. The challenge is great to have all-round socio-economic development, which has a bearing on scientific achievements. Rajiv Gandhi shared his visionary ideas on Science and the Future of Mankind, with the scientific community, while delivering the inaugural address at the 75th Session of the Indian Science Congress Association on Pune, on 7 January 1988. He said – "In my view, the most critical one is the frontier of human well-being. Addressing the Indian Science Congress Association, 40 years ago, Pandit Nehru said: "Surely, science is not merely an individual's search for truth. It is something infinitely more than ... Its objective must be to remove the ills of the community. It must have a social objective before it.

Rajiv Gandhi strove for excellence and perfection. While giving away the Sir Shanti Swarup Bhatnagar Awards for Science and Technology on 27 February 1986 in New Delhi, he said that–

> *We have a good infrastructure of scientific institutions. Funding is not too much of a problem. Our achievements, whether in the agricultural sciences, atomic energy or space, are very highly commendable. But it is still odd that with so much better facilities than those available to Bose, Raman, Sahni or Bhabha, we are not able to produce that level of work. There can be no shortcoming in our scientists. We have proved that in India, and our scientists have proved that when they go out of India. We have to get to the key of this*

key of this problem if our science is to compete with the science in the most advanced nations, which is a must if India is to go the way we want her to go.

We can achieve world leadership in key areas by refocusing our strategies on areas that we feel are more relevant or necessary to us, or areas that we want to go ahead in, and, maybe, reduce our efforts in those areas, which we find of less significance. Of course, we would like to give the same thrust and push in all areas, but being a developed country with constraints, we cannot go out in every field that is interesting or even needed. To this end, we have developed a new strategy, which, we hope, will give you new energy for your work. We are dividing them into missions and thrust areas. Basically, the idea is to identify specific areas where we want really top grade work. They may be for a social objective – drinking water, oilseeds, and illiteracy. They may be in highly technical areas – fusion, lasers. We may want to do some work in blue-sky areas of fundamental research.

"If in the current shift in global relationships, we are not able to ensure for India her rightful place; we may miss a good opportunity. We may not get an opportunity for decades to come to correct this situation. So, we should not miss this opportunity. It will require tightening our belts, reducing wasteful expenditure, whether it is in Government or whether it is elsewhere, and focusing all our energies on the main task of removing poverty, of getting India, where it should be to its rightful place in the leadership of world civilization" said Rajiv Gandhi at the Sir Shanti Swarup Bhatnagar Award giving ceremony on 17 October 1988.

New Vision of Humanity

"Indian science must always strive to be at the frontiers of knowledge. That was our traditional place before we got colonized and all our expertise got killed. We must get back to that peak, to that high position. Our science must be innovative and not imitative. It is not adequate just to replicate what others have done; we must effect breakthroughs so that others replicate what we have done.

"Scientific activity is a creative activity and like all creative activities, it needs the right atmosphere, a congenial atmosphere, for that creativity to take place. We must help develop just such an atmosphere in our institutions to allow the spirit of creativity to flourish. If we are to get top class work from our top class scientists, then we must see that all the red tape is removed, all the inputs that are required are readily available and that advanced centers of research and development on science are allowed to flourish in every sphere of activity and in every part of our country. But at the same time, scientists must not get locked up in ivory towers doing their research just for the sake of science, for the sake of research, especially in fields such as agricultural research. That research must relate very actively to the reality of the life of the average person in our country, the life of the poorest, to those areas which are of utmost importance to the nation.

"The linkages between science and its applications between science in one particular field and science in other fields, and even the linkage between science and humanities is very important if science is to fulfill the role expected of it.

"We need a new vision of humanity, a vision based on truth and non-violence, a vision that will nourish life in all its myriad beautiful forms. That vision can have no place for nuclear weapons. That vision can have no room for the mass human suicide represented by nuclear weapons. In the unfolding of this vision the spiritual experience of humankind must play its part. It is an experience of love, of breaking away from one's own narrow grooves, of reaching out beyond oneself, of exploring the infinite possibilities of Self. Science must begin to answer the questions that real men and women pose, not only in one country but in all countries. In seeking to do so, it will inevitably assist the yearning of the human spirit for peace, for harmony and for truth. Then and then alone will science lead us, as our scriptures remind us, from ignorance to knowledge, from darkness to light and from death to immortality". Rajiv Gandhi said at the valedictory session of the International Symposium on Science, Technology and Development on 25 March 1987. He further said – *As scientists, you have the power to show us the way. You are not only men and women of science, you are citizens of the human race endowed with unique ability. You are able to understand the physical world better than others. You have the means to transform it. You owe it to humankind that this special gift is used in the service of peace.*

On the issue of world peace and disarmament, Rajiv Gandhi said in his valedictory address, at the 75th session of the Indian Science Congress Association held at Pune on 7 January 1988, that –

> *With the signing of the treaty to abolish intermediate nuclear forces, we have at least a ray of light from under the darkness of the nuclear cloud. That, at last, the concern for man and his destiny is not quite dead. ... We have to remember that eventually we are of one world. Far from being insulated from it, we are a part of the global scientific environment. Nor are we immune from the mistakes and madness of others. Science and technology have taken us to the brink of nuclear war. We must pull back.*

Delivering the Nehru Centenary Memorial Lecture, on 13 November 1989, Rajiv Gandhi said —"We believe that far from imitating models developed elsewhere, it is the mission of India to build, in the light of the precepts given to us by Gandhiji and Panditji, a society and a Nation which would serve as an example to the world on how to deal with the post-nuclear world and the new technology that now lies in human hands. Nuclear technology has given humankind the power to destroy itself and our planet Earth in the briefest wink of history. Technology has also opened unparalleled opportunities for a fulfilling and bountiful life for all the citizens of planet Earth. How is one to avoid the former fate and ensure the latter? The answer lies in the human mind. Panditji's vision of India encompassed our millennial past and looked out to a millennial future. It was not conditioned by immediate problems and immediate concerns. Rather, it drew its inspiration from the essential continuities of India's civilization. It charted its perspectives from the need to restore India to its position in the vanguard of all that is of the best in human civilization. [11]

> *The relationship between villages and town has been one of the earliest problems of civilization. Etymologically, the very word civilization connotes urbanization and has not given attention to a comprehensive study of rural problems. Gandhiji (Mahatma Gandhi) was tireless in pointing out that the freedom and progress of India was synonymous with the self-government and economic regeneration of its villages. Maintaining that* **"If the village perishes, India perishes too"***, he did not want cities to live off villages. His economic ideas were designed to provide more work for rural people. He was not against machinery as such but against machines which forced idleness on rural hands. He did not object to villages using even modern machines and tools, provided the self-reliant character of rural industry was not jettisoned. In the West, the evolution of the machinery was motivated by the desire to displace labour. But Gandhiji was for production by the masses, as distinguished from mass production, in its common connotation. ... Modernity does not imply alienation,*

said Mrs. Indira Gandhi, at the Science Congress on 3 January 1976 at Waltair.[12]

The power of technology greatly fascinated Rajiv and more than anybody else, he instilled the imperative of upgrading obsolete production processes and adopting technological innovation if the Indian entrepreneurs were to survive in the face of global competition. He repeatedly reminded the people that the 21st century would be dominated by electronics and telecommunications and India must keep pace with the new developments to hold her own. [13]

References

1. Sonia Gandhi – Rajiv, Viking – Penguin Books India (P) Ltd., New Delhi, p. 4, 1992.
2. P. Sood – Rajiv Gandhi: The Brave New Leader, Marwah Publications, New Delhi, pp. 51-52,1986.
3. Satyawrat Ponkshe – Rajiv Gandhi: The Pragmatic Prime Minister of India, Bhate – Ponkshe Publications, Pune, pp. 331, 1986.
4. Kathelene Healy: Rajiv Gandhi – The years of Power, p7-8, Vikas Publishing House Pvt. Lrd., New Delhi 1989.
5. Jawahar Lal Nehru – Speeches Vol. III, Ministry of Information and Broadcasting, Govt. of India, New Delhi, p. 35 (6 October 1955) 1958.
6. Sonia Gandhi – Rajiv, Viking – Penguin Books India (P) Ltd., p.104, New Delhi, 1992.
7. Indira Gandhi – Inaugural Address, Indian Science Congress Association, Waltair, 3 January, 1978.
8. Indira Gandhi – Inaugural Address, Indian Science Congress Association, Bombay, 3 January, 1969.
9. Indira Gandhi – Inaugural Address, Indian Science Congress Association, Bangalore, 3 January, 1971.
10. Jawahar Lal Nehru – The Discovery of India, Meridian Books Limited, (VIII), pp. 385-385, London, 1951.
11. Rajiv Gandhi – Selected Speeches and Writings, Vol. I-V, (1984 – 1989), Publications Division, Ministry of Information and Broadcasting, Government of India, New Delhi, 1989.
12. Pawam Sikka —Rajiv Gandhi : Selected Speeches on Science and Technology, Uppal Publishing House, Delhi 2007
13. S. S. Gill – The Dynasty, Harper Collins Publishers India, New Delhi, pp. 396-400, 1996.

2

Rajiv Gandhi Era: Science and the Government of India

.........The foundations of our scientific and technological developments were laid many years ago by Panditji and a major thrust was given to our science and technology by Indiraji. It is on this base, that we are able to use our science and technology to help the poorest people in our country. Indian scientists have shown that they are upto the best in the world when it comes to developing technology and when comes to taking our nation forward.

—Rajiv Gandhi
Speech in the Lok Sabha, 10 April 1986

Rajiv Gandhi was elected the seventh Prime Minister of India in 1984. He brought with him a brightness and hope, as well as a believable vision of the 21st century India- qualities then badly needed to speed up the process for achieving techno-economic development of India. He was a sincere, earnest and soft-spoken person and a thorough gentleman. Though a reluctant entrant in to politics, having made the crucial choice he never looked back.

He was stated to be a man in hurry, aspiring to make India – a technologically advanced and developed nation by the next two decades with the inputs of modern science and technology. He projected an image of modernity and infused a new confidence among people, which was marked by a vision largely technocratic and relying heavily on science and technology. His modern outlook, clear vision and abiding faith in science and technology was for eradicating poverty and for providing good quality life to the people.

Rajiv Gandhi, the youngest ever Prime Minister of India, brought a new powerful dynamism to an ancient India. This, coupled with his global vision, saw him leading India towards the 21st century. He outlined his tasks ahead:

> *Our task today is to bring India to the threshold of the 21st century – free of the burden of the poverty, legacy of our colonial past and capable of meeting the rising aspirations of our people. This will require sustained efforts on our part.*

Rajiv Gandhi's interests and concerns were multifaceted and comprehensive. He made all efforts to transform India – a nation conceived as traditional and backward into a modern scientific and technology savvy one. He recognised the importance of science and technology for the economic development of the society. For this purpose, during his dynamic years, he adopted a four-pronged approach, viz:

(i) The Mission Approach,
(ii) Integration of Science and Technology in the Socio – economic Sectors,
(iii) Application of Science and Technology for Rural Development and Poverty Alleviation; and
(iv) Science and Technology for Societal Development (to benefit the specific targets).

He wanted to usher the country into the new millennium at home and abroad and visualized top of the world position for India and the Indians. The New Education Policy introduced by him in 1986 was an attempt to give higher education a new vitality by integrating it with the practical needs of society. It was looked upon as an instrument for shaping future of India. It laid stress on vocationalisation and also on non-formal or distance education. Education and development are inter-related.

One of the first things Rajiv Gandhi did on becoming PM was to formulate a *new computer policy*. The main thrust of this policy was to rapidly increase the use of computers in offices, banks, railways and other such establishments. He therefore, encouraged the indigenous manufacture of computers by reducing duties on components. His own example had a powerful impact and it soon became a status symbol to own a personal computer. Concrete benefits from computerization were already apparent during Rajiv's regime. The "Electronics City" of Bangalore, the Indian version of 'Silicon Valley', developed fast and became a growing point for the development of electronics industry. He had placed high hopes on the software production and it has already become India's leading foreign exchange earner. An integrated computer network for the railways, RAILNET, was created for computerized reservations and keeping track of wagon movement. The Indian Banks Association also then opted for computerization of its entire accounting system, but NICNET is the most important computer network, which provides countrywide linkages right down to the district level for the storage, processing, retrieval and exchange of data between the various government departments and field agencies.[1]

Science in the Nation Building

Jawaharlal Nehru recognized long ago that political freedom would be incomplete without economic independence and the economic independence would be beyond our grasp without scientific self-reliance. National laboratories and central institutes were established because national problems needed homegrown answers, said Mrs. Indira Gandhi.[2]

We regard science as a powerful instrument of social change. Modernization is not merely production through improved technology. It means changing the nation. Science is as greatly needed for improving production as for doing good to society in other ways. It implies the best use of material and human resources, of equipment and social organizations, so as to bring about the possible diffusion of welfare. Human welfare should not recognize national boundaries, but in the world as it is organized today, we have to still think in terms of what Government can do for their people, said Mrs. Indira Gandhi, at Science Congress Session, on 3 January 1970 at Kharagpur.

Rajiv Gandhi, as Prime Minister of India, as well as Cabinet Minister-in-charge of Science and Technology portfolio (1984-89), took major initiatives so that scientific and technological capabilities were brought to bear appropriately on problems clearly defined on the basis of national objectives and needs of the society. With a view to keeping an eye, on the development of technology, besides prime ministership, he himself retained the portfolios of science and technology, electronics, atomic energy, space, environment and forest, and ocean development departments.. In his great endeavour of building new India, he sought partnership between scientists and the Government for infusing science – consciousness in the decision-making process of the Government.

As a deviation from the past of constituting apex science advisory bodies for the Cabinet, he set up a Science Advisory Council to the Prime Minister (SAC – P) on 4th February 1986, under the chairmanship of eminent scientist Prof. C.N.R. Rao, to render him advice on:

(a) Major issues facing science and technology today,
(b) The health of science in the country and the directions in which it should move, and
(c) A perspective plan for 2001 A.D.

Rajiv Gandhi gave full support to the recommendations of the SAC – P by setting up an apex body called the National Science and Technology Council for coordinating the programmes and activities related to Science and Technology in the socio – economic sectors. In addition, he appointed Prof. MGK Menon, the then Member (Science), Planning Commission as a Scientific

Advisor, as well as Mr. Sam Pitroda, Chairman, C – DOT as an Advisor to the Prime Minister on Technology Missions.

A Council for Social Audit, under the Chairmanship of the former Chief Justice of the Supreme Court, Mr. Justice P. N. Bhagwati was set up in July 1988 to monitor the implementation of the programmes of the National Technology Missions. The Council acted as a mechanism to increase people's participation in the Missions, conduct qualitative assessments, perform concurrent evaluations, suggest improvements of delivery and heighten people's awareness. It was a "watch-dog" system of credible and objective feed back for assessing the success or failure of the five technology missions, which were at the various stages of implementations, at that time, in the country.

Institutionalization of Science and Technology

Jawahar Lal Nehru, the great visionary for shaping India's destiny, was of the firm conviction that it is science alone that can solve the problems of hunger and poverty .... . Guided by this conviction, he went ahead and set up many R & D laboratories, scientific and technical institutions, during his regime 1947 – 1964, in the fields of scientific and technological, industrial, agricultural and medical, all over India under the aegis of CSIR, ICAR, ICMR and DRDO respectively. Mrs. Indira Gandhi, also a visionary like her father, set up, for the first time in the history of India, a separate Department of Science and Technology (DST) with a view to promoting science and technology, as well as, undertaking its activities in the new and emerging fields, in the country.

The awareness of the benefits of science and technology then became part of our national policy and concerted efforts were made to institutionalize it. With a view to providing new thrust to the development of emerging fields like Biotechnology, Environment, Ocean sciences, Industrial research and Non – conventional energy sources, Rajiv Gandhi created separate Departments / Ministries for each one of the above disciplines in 1985 – 86, under the Government of India. These departments were

were bifurcated from the (mother) Department of Science and Technology, where they existed in the nucleus form, since 1972. For example, he constituted:

- Department of Biotechnology
- Department of Environment
  (later upgraded to the Ministry of Environment and Forests)
- Department of Ocean Development
- Department of Scientific and Industrial Research
- Department of Non – Conventional Energy Sources
  (later upgraded to the level of Ministry)

Rajiv Gandhi, while introducing far-reaching changes in the administrative set up of the government created a full-fledged Ministry of Science and Technology, in 1985, comprising Departments of Science and Technology (DST), Bio-technology (DBT) and Scientific and Industrial Research (DSIR). This creation was in keeping with his desire to take the country into the 21st century by building the necessary scientific and technological infrastructure. The DSIR was assigned to look after the matters relating to National Research Development Corporation (NRDC), Central Electronics Limited (CEL) and National Information System for Science and Technology (NISSAT) for effecting greater coordination in scientific research and technological development (R&D) as well as upgradation of technology in the country. Besides, he established a foresight – agency in 1988 i.e. Technology Information, Forecasting and Assessment Council (TIFAC), New Delhi to prepare Status Reports and Monographs, Vision -2020 documents etc. on various subjects of socio-economic relevance to India's growth, and for identifying their strengths and weaknesses, as well as, the scopes for attaining excellence by applying science and technology.

With a view to sharing of scientific and technological efforts with other countries, for the welfare of mankind, Rajiv Gandhi also set up –

- A Center for Science and Technology for Non – Aligned and other Developing Countries, New Delhi

- An Indo – French Center for the Promotion of Advanced Scientific Research, New Delhi, and
- A National Informatics Centre, New Delhi,

towards accelerating international cooperation in Science and Technology. He also constituted a Special All India Congress Committee Cell on Science and Technology, to inculcate a sense of commitment in these fields at the party level.

"The core of the problem in our development process is the gap between what India can do and what India is doing" - he said in Parliament in 1986. He believed that it was necessary to pursue basic research at the highest level (what he referred to as the blue skies research) to promote competence in the new and emerging areas and to attain excellence. He set up an apex body on the *National Super – Conductivity Programme*, to enable India to have a lead in this new and emerging field.

"We have a strong base in agriculture, and in industry and a significant scientific infrastructure in terms of numbers, range of skills and quality in India. There exists a foundation for self – reliance". In his address to the 73rd Session of the Indian Science Congress Association, on 7 January 1986, at New Delhi, Rajiv Gandhi said-

> *Our scientists must concentrate on what is most meaningful for a country like India. In today's circumstances that means in the rural areas, the agriculture sector and the various sectors that support our agriculture and rural industry. Our scientists have considerable achievements to their credit during these past years. They have put India in a strong, self-reliant position, not just in agriculture but also in certain strategic and sensitive areas where it was difficult for us to import technology. Where there have been real challenges, where the chips have been down, our scientists have risen to the occasion and have shown the world that they are second to none when it comes to capability, competence and achievement.*

Today the challenge that our scientists and technologists face is greater than the challenge that our scientists faced a couple of thousand of years ago. The challenge now is not just to catch up with, to equal, what is going on in the rest of the world, but the challenge is to surpass and once more give a lead that we used to some thousand of years ago.

The Prime Minister Rajiv Gandhi, while addressing a meeting of the "Consultative Committee of Members of Parliament", attached to the Scientific Departments, outlined the programme of Government of employing science and technology for the human resource development. Rajiv Gandhi – the techno-crat Prime Minister of India, also presided over the then rapidly growing space programme. India's first scientific experiment payload, 'Anuradha' was launched on 30 April 1985 by a US space shuttle from Kennedy Space Centre, Florida, U.S.A. He desired self-sufficiency in satellites and launch vehicles alike, rather than continuing to rely on NASA, Ariane and Soviet launchers. India should use its own ASLV 68lbs pay-load launcher, as early as possible, before going to a larger Ariane type PSLV in 1990 – which could also make an ICBM, provided small modifications were affected in its fourth stage, according to Prof. Satish Dhawan – one of India's foremost space-scientist.

Rajiv Gandhi set up a Ministry of Environment to prepare and enforce environment protection regime. It was made mandatory for industrial projects, other polluting undertakings and Dams to obtain "Clearance from Environmental Angle", from this Ministry before going ahead with the project. His most ambitious and comprehensive initiative at the ground level was the creation of six "technology missions". These missions were assigned the task of applying technology to six well-defined areas of under-development to achieve specific time-bound results.

1. The Drinking Water Mission was to make potable water available to all the Indian villages according to a set timetable.

2. The Literacy Mission was expected to speedily improve literacy levels and use satellite linked communication aids like radio and television for imparting mass education. The Government promulgated a three-pronged approach to improve matters: The literacy Mission was assigned the task of achieving 100 percent literacy by the time India entered the 21st century, Secondly, to rapidly expand facilities for vocational training, so as to tackle the problem of the unemployed and lastly to launch *'Operation Blackboard'* to provide basic amenities and teaching aids in all the schools. He laid particular stress on extending the concept of "distant education" through radio and T.V. and established the Indira Gandhi National Open University (IGNOU) for providing well-designed educational material to those who could not attend colleges.
3. A nation-wide immunization programme for children and pregnant women was launched to cover the entire population.
4. Another mission was designed to usher in the white revolution, by increasing the supply of milk and other dairy products through improving the stock of milch cattle and eradicating diseases of livestock.
5. As the country was spending large amount of foreign exchange on importing edible oils, a separate mission was set up to develop and introduce improved varieties of oil seeds.
6. And, lastly, in view of the increasing importance of communications, a technology mission was set up for indigenous manufacture of telecom so as to bring the telephone within the reach of all villagers. He realized the importance of telecommunication and computerization and laid the foundation for a well-connected India. He established -

- Low power transmitter network right down to the grassroots level.
- Rapid computerization of telephone exchanges and availability of telephone on demand.
- The pioneer of IT and communication revolution in India.

- Reach the benefits of research done previously to the people in a systematic and phased manner.

Rajiv Gandhi said that a lot of thanking had gone into the creation of these missions and there is no doubt that the areas of under development identified by the government merited urgent attention. Even after forty years of Independence (1987), 28 percent of villagers had no access to drinking water, half the population was still illiterate, millions of children and expectant mothers perished for want of elementary health care, per capita milk consumption was only 160 grams per day, and the country was not producing enough cooking oil to meet its bare requirements. In a foreword to the Seventh Plan document (1985—90), Rajiv Gandhi made it clear that-

> *"Planning has given as a strong base for building a modern, self-reliant industrial economy. Indian industry today is highly diversified, producing a wide range of products, many embodying a high level of technology. We have a broad entrepreneurial base and ample technological and managerial manpower. But some weaknesses have also become evident. Much of our industry suffers from high cost. Inadequate attention is paid to quality. In many areas, we are working with a technology that is obsolete. We have reached a watershed in our industrial development and in the next phase, we must concentrate on overcoming these problems. Our emphasis must be on greater efficiency, reduction of cost and improvement of quality. This calls for absorption of new technology, greater attention to economies of scale and greater competition."*

Rajiv Gandhi said, in the Lok Sabha, on 22 January 1985, that- "India's economy is very largely that of the farmer. We shall be doing many things for our farmers in the coming years. We have to see that our agricultural output increases substantially.

We have to see that the inputs to the farmers are available at proper prices. We have to see that the procurement prices are correct. It is only then that we shall be able to get this growth that we want. We shall look into this. I hope we shall see a sharp increase in our agricultural production.

"We will be looking, as the President said earlier, Sir, into the textile industry. Over the years, the textile industry has deteriorated very substantially and when I talk about the textile industry, I include the handlooms and the weavers from the lowest level to the highest mechanized level of the industry. We have to develop a new policy which does not throw anybody out of a job but we must remember that our textile policy is not targeted at producing jobs but producing cloth and producing cloth at rates which are acceptable to the poor people, to the masses, in our country. We will try and achieve this.

"We are looking at a new industrial policy. We have to realize that India in the past 35 years has progressed tremendously in spite of everything our friends across said. We have made tremendous progress and now we must look ahead to a bright future. If our industry is to progress, if our industry is to keep up with industry in the rest of the world, it must operate under similar conditions. We shall look at it from this end. We have to think of employment. Industry is not necessarily the best place for employment. Sometimes, it is the most inefficient place for employment. We have to look at how we can increase employment even more that industry can give us. I am not advocating closing down industries but a radical charge is needed in all the industries that we have.

"Our education policy, our industrial policy and our trade policy must be such that they look ahead to taking India into the future with the rest of the world. We cannot pretend to be equal to other countries when we are operating systems, which are 20 years or 10 years out of date. The world today is moving very fast. We shall introduce a new education policy, which will be targeted at a more modern type of employment."

NATIONAL POLICY DECLARATIONS ON SCIENCE AND TECHNOLOGY ANNOUNCED DURING THE RAJIV GANDHI ERA

1. The Computer Policy, India	19 Nov 1984
2. Statement on Textile Policy	June 1985
3. The Environment (Protection) Act, 1986	23 May 1986
4. National Policy on Education, 1986	May 1986
5. The Research and Development Cess Act, 1986	14 August 1986
6. National Water Policy	1987
7. New Policy on Seed Development, 1988	16 Sep 1988
8. National Forest Policy, 1988	7 December 1988
9. New Industrial Policy, 1988	1988
10. Drug Distribution Policy, 1988	1988.

New Perspectives and Scientific Developments

Science is regarded as a powerful instrument of social change. Modernisation is not merely production through improved technology. It means changing the old concept of welfare of the nation. Science is as greatly needed for improving production as for doing good to society in other ways. It implies the best use of material and human resources of equipment and social organization so as to bring about the widest possible diffusion of welfare, said Mrs Indira Gandhi.[3] Soon, after assuming the Prime Ministership, Rajiv Gandhi had , promised the nation a Government that worked faster. He also declared that he wanted to lead India into the 21st century. He chartered a route map for making a strong and vibrant India. He emphasized the use of Science and Technology in the day-to-day life so that India could emerge as a technologically advanced and self-sufficient nation in the 21st century.

Here are some quotes / excerpts from his speeches on certain key areas:

1. Science Administration in India

.........We have a very substantial scientific and technological base. We have to look ahead to see how India which is at a turning point will develop......

.........Our scientific and technological institutions do not allow young minds to come out to the fore. There is an administrative or may be a bureaucratic block and some how this has to be overcome, if we are to really progress......

.........One of the problems in India has been with our scientists' salary, their facilities, their perks, even more important with recognition they get......

.........This really means that what we are looking is much better scientific administration. Scientific administration must be a subject of its own. It cannot be borrowed from general administration. ......At the same time, the answer is not to find the best scientist and put him in-charge as an administrator because then we lose a scientist. It is a very specialized task and we have not developed people in this area, and we must see how we can develop this.

.........What are the qualities that are needed, what sort of training and direction are required to produce this cadre of people, who would really support our scientists and our laboratories.

.........It is only when we are able to work in this manner that we will be striving for world leadership in a number of fields.

.........Well, it is when this basic attitude changes in Government that our scientists will be giving us the results we are looking for. (see page 66 onwards, for more details on the subject).

2. Brain – Drain

.........Every developing country needs scientific manpower, if it is to develop and move out of the developing category into the developed one.

*.........Mention has been made of brain – drain. This is one of our major problems, but I see it differently. ....or as I prefer to call it **the brain – bank**.*

.........If we are to stop brain – drain of the so many scientists and technologists leaving the country, we have to tailor the subjects, that we are teaching to the needs of our development.

.........We must produce the atmosphere, the infrastructure for it in industry, in our research establishments, in our academic institutions. And, we are attempting to do this. But in any developing country, this does take time.

.........If we are to utilize the brains that are available in India, we must create an environment in which they can work. An environment which promotes mediocrity cannot be an environment in which excellence can flourish.

.........It is only then that Indians, many in very high positions in the forefront of technologies and research, will want to come back and help in our work. ......For the development of India, for our progress. *(see page 72 onwards for more details on the subject).*

3. Agriculture and Rural Development

.........Agriculture is the most important part of our economy and of our development process. ......we have to see how we can develop agriculture to break the hold of poverty.

.........One of the biggest challenges that we are facing is that of drought and, some areas, very severe floods. These underline the need to link the scientific effort with the reality as it exists on the ground.

.........The areas where we would like the concentration are the semi-arid areas – the zones where the productivity is very low, where poverty is still a very major problem.

.........Perhaps the one key factor for better agricultural productivity is land reforms. ......we are committed to tackle this problem and see that land reforms do take place and take place effectively.

........., And we will be coming out with a programme which we will implement hopefully fast.

.........When we talk of high technology today, we are talking about bio – engineering, we are talking of better implements, better tools. We are talking of better forecast for the rains.

.........Besides the announcement of National Seed Policy in 1986, bold steps were taken to aid the farmers such as – restoration of credit facility from NABARD; short – term production credit; special credits for rain – fed farming; and issuing of Pass – Books and Credit Cards for the farmers.

.........The time has come to reiterate that the highest national priority must be given to the farmer, to farming, to food and agriculture as the corner – stone of our economy. Therefore, we are determined to accord highest priority to agriculture in the Eighth Five-Year Plan (1990 – 95). (See page 111 for more details)

4. Technology Missions in Selected fields

Rajiv Gandhi was the prime mover of the vitally important Technology Missions in selected fields, in India. He said -

.........We have come out with the idea of having Missions. ......now my concept of Missions was limited number of fields with very specific targets.

.........Ten areas in five years or ten years and we will be the leaders in technology or in science in those particular areas. ......we try to target those areas in directions that will give us a direct fall out.

.........The concept is that we would give much more freedom, remove all the strings in these areas, give proper funding to see that we can make real progress as we did in space, as we did in Atomic energy...... .

.........We have set up a number of Missions, which start with the frontiers of Science and hopefully will end up in the homes of our people, in their daily lives. If India is to win this struggle against poverty, it is only with the most modern and best methods that we stand a chance. We look forward to you and other scientists like you to help us in this giant step that the country has to take. *(see page 138 for more details on the subject)*

5. Development of Scientific Temper

.........Panditji set the mood for developing a scientific temper in the country. It was not an easy task at that time with a newly independent, very poor country, to strike out in such a direction.

.........But Panditji had the vision to realize that it was only with science and technology that India could lift itself up and today we are where we are because Panditji and Indiraji put that thrust in Science and Technology.

.........Ultimately what will help us to develop a real base for science and technology is an involvement of the average person with science and technology, whether it is a question of appliances, that he is using at home, whether it is in the fields where farmer is using technology.

.........Unless, this scientific temper, as Panditji said, really seeps down to our society, we will never be able to get the inputs for science that are within our capability, which are available to us, but are just not being allowed to develop.

.........We have not gone from a scientific temper to industrialization but we have industrialization leading to a scientific temper. Therefore there is too much a race which leads to imitation and too little innovation. We need to break out of this rut.

.........We are looking at this from the starting point and that is our New Education Policy. (see page143 for more details on the subject.

6. Computer Revolution in India

.........India missed the industrial revolution, it cannot afford to miss the computer revolution.

.........The first policy, Rajiv Gandhi announced after taking over as the Prime Minister of India, in late 1984, was the Computer Policy – earning for him the reputation of a man who would take India in to the 21st century.

.........The Industrial Revolution led to a gap between the developed and the developing one. The information revolution today is enlarging that gap.

......That is why, it is all the more important that for communication and take information technology, we take leap forward ......to set on to the front – line technology.........I have no doubt that with the know – how we have, we can show the developed countries that Indians can come up, can beat them at their own game, compete with them in their own areas. (See page 182 for deatails)

7. Environmental Protection

.........Industry is not taking the responsibility of protecting the environment from its side effects. This responsibility must be squarely fixed on the industry.

.........We have enacted certain laws which do not allow certain types of industries to come up in certain areas.

.........No major project can even start unless it has full environmental clearance.

.........Most of our training and education (to the foresters) dates back to the British time. ......A bureaucratic approach cannot work, especially where we are dealing with people; with the social system.

.........We start accusing the tribals of doing all sorts of things in the forests, forgetting that they have lived in these forests for hundreds and thousands of years......Perhaps the problem is not what the tribals do but we ourselves do in their name.

.....Although the poor bear the brunt of environmental damage, they are themselves little responsible for any of that damage. For centuries they have lived in harmony with nature. The problem is caused by large-scale commercial exploitation, which garners the profits but escapes the consequences.

.........The international community must also address itself to safety measures in high-risk industries.

.........Problems of development and the environment can only be resolved through cooperative international action. *(see page 148 onwards for more details on the subject).*

8. Eradication of Poverty

> ....*We must remember that the primary problem that we face in India is one of removing poverty and keeping in mind that the litmus test for any national activity is how it helps us remove poverty.*
>
> ....*We have developed a number of technology missions to carry out just this task, to direct the high technology and scientific developments towards removing poverty, and the war on poverty.*
>
> ....*If India is to win this struggle against poverty, it is only with the most modern and best methods that we stand a chance.*
>
> ....*What we are looking for is to use the most modern technology for the benefits of the poorest and the most depressed in our country.* *(See page 200 for more details on the subject).*

RURAL – URBAN INDIA

Jawahar Lal Nehru defined the role of science and technology in terms of the poor and the people at large. He said: *It is science alone that can solve the problems of hunger and poverty, of insanitation, of illiteracy, of superstition and deadening custom and tradition, of vast resources running to waste, of a rich country inhabited by starving people.*

Rajiv Gandhi, in his Nehru Memorial Lecture, delivered on 13 November 1989, in New Delhi, said that – Jawahar Lal Nehru *was "convinced that the rapid industrialization of India is essential to relieve the pressure on the land, to combat poverty and to raise standards of living, for defence, and a variety of other purposes".* The short-cut might have been to concentrate industrialization where infrastructure was readily available. This we did not do. We spread it in two ways. One, by undertaking different types of industrialization ranging from cottage, village and small industry to more sophisticated larger units. Second, by extending industrialization to remote, backward areas through incentives and governmental fiat. In particular, the public sector has played a notable part in opening out the hinterland, in bringing all of India within the purview of industrialization. We have thus avoided any unbridgeable chasm widening between industrial India and agricultural India, between rural India and urban India and traditional India, between one part of India and any other part of India.

"The Green Revolution, which brought the prospect of progress to millions of our farmers, was in essence a revolution of science and technology, taking the results of the most sophisticated genetic sciences to the farmer tilling the soil. In the rainfed areas, we have a Technology Mission on Oilseeds and Edible Oils as well as a National Project on Pulses. A White Revolution – dairying and milk products – is now sweeping parts of the nation. In the hills, a horticulture revolution is in the making. In a similar vein, we have started a new initiative to harness technology to the service of the most pressing needs of the poor, such as immunization, drinking water, flood control and the eradication of illiteracy." Rajiv Gandhi said in the Lok Sabha on 10 April 1986, that – *Where science and technology is concerned, we must keep in mind that nothing but the best will do for the country; and we must work towards that end. With everybody's support, I believe we will be able to do it.*

The Techno-crat Prime Minister : The influx of rational Technology in the most pragmatic atmosphere, provided the basic working philosophy of Rajiv Gandhi's administration of whether it was the development of human resources or attaining self-reliance in energy or food production or anti-poverty or any other aspect of development. This futuristic thrust became the leit motif of his agenda for change. And, naturally the team of advisors he assembled, also comprised young talented persons in line with the corporate culture of a modern industrial society. [1] He was crystal clear in his approach to the target. ...*together we will build an India of 21st century.*

Rajiv Gandhi was alive towards the development of weaker sections of Indian society – and remained committed to ending the problem of unemployment and alleviating poverty. The revolutionary visionary steps taken by him for strengthening the development of science and technology in the country and making it self – sufficient during his dynamic years will continue to inspire and lead us towards a better way of life.

References

1. S. S. Gill – The Dynasty, p. 396 – 400, Harper Collins Publishers India, New Delhi, 1996.
2. Indira Gandhi, Inaugural Address, Indian Science Congress Association, Mysore, 1982.
3. Indira Gandhi, Inaugural Address, Indian Science Congress Association, Kharagpur, 3 January 1970.
4. Indira Gandhi, Inaugural Address, Indian Science Congress Association, Tirupati, 3 January 1983.

EXCERPT FROM AN INTERVIEW
RAJIV GANDHI ON SCIENCE AND THE GOVERNMENT

Q: *In the field of tele-communication, Mr. Prime Minister, you would perhaps remember that you had called Mr. Thomas Kora to your residence and asked him to dial 100 and he could not get it. Now you promised in those days, and of course your mother had also promised earlier, that the telephone system would be improved in the country and perhaps an agreement was signed with a French company and a factory in Gonda has been installed to manufacture electronic exchanges.*

My first question would be: What are you doing for the second factory and whether the country is going in for another technology in the field of telecommunication, which has the worst infrastructure in the country.

R.G.: One, we are looking very seriously at communications. But, as you are aware, we are under tremendous resource constraints during this period. The specific question of what has been happening about the second telephone factory, you better talk to the Communications Minister. He will be able to answer that better.

But as a matter of policy, what we are developing is our own technology. We are hopeful that it will be as good as or better than what is available anywhere in the world. We have got the best brains working on it and we are optimistic.

Q: *Here is an inter related question. You see the talented are not nurtured in our country and they are going abroad. That is called Brain Drain. What is being done to curb this...?*

R.G.: Well, the only real way to stop it is to have enough opportunity available in our country. That will come when we develop more. As we develop, opportunities open up and more and more people come back. But to take every one back will take a long time. And then do we really want to get everyone back? We want to get them back eventually. We do want them to go abroad to get that experience, because you know, we can't give that experience. And, education does not finish at university. Education continues throughout your life. So, I feel it is necessary that a certain number of people do go out, get more experience and then we make opportunities for them to come back. So we can use not just their education, but also their experience.

Q: *Are you in favour of introducing computer education in every school in India?*

R.G.: We could not afford to do that, even if we wanted to. But we have introduced in a little over 400 schools. These are average schools, right out in the districts and the villages and the response so far, has been very good. We will enlarge this programme. We feel that there must be adequate opportunity for our children to be involved with computers, to learn how to live with them.

Q: *During the last three decades, India has moved from a land of famine to one of agricultural surplus. Are the prospects now encouraging from your view, that your economy will be able to stand on that agricultural base and to begin supporting high technological and industrial development?*

R. G. *Yes, definitely. And we are looking this now. We have already made substantial studies, like I said earlier, space technology. Of course, we can't compete with the U.S., but in our own small way, we have a modest programme. And it is working well.*

In certain areas of high technology, we have done fairly well. And, this means, well, we have to be very careful that don't get carried away with the glamour of high technology and go off a tangent. High technology must be such that it helps the average Indian to improve his lot and that is how we will be looking at high technology.

---

* *(Excerpts from the Press Conferences. Ref: A Portrait of Ragiv Gandhi, Shrikant Verma, Arnold Heinemann, New Delhi, p. 98, 1985).*

3

New Initiatives of Rajiv Gandhi His Action Plan of Modernizing India

> *......The time has come for us to take a stock and see what we need to do to quicken the pace of our progress. We need to do this across the board. We must therefore do this in the context of science and technology as well...... I would urge you to consider what the scientific community and the authority must do in the coming years to meet the challenge......*
>
> **—Rajiv Gandhi**
> **Indian Science Congress Association, Pune**
> **7 January, 1988**

The future of our society, its development and direction is vitally linked with the activities of our scientists and technologists, said Mrs. Indira Gandhi, at the 58th Session, Indian Science Congress Association, Bangalore, on January 1971. She further said ... Man's wants go beyond his needs. We in India must attempt to readapt technology and place man and his spirit at the center of science. It is up to us to see that in the pursuit of the natural necessities of life, we do not lose our human values, or our distinctiveness as individuals and as a nation. To find this new path is perhaps the greatest challenge to Indian scientists and technologists.

Mrs. Indira Gandhi, further said at the Science Congress, Nagpur, on 3 January 1974 that ... *this comprehensive approach to science and technology will encourage greater participation by our scientists and technologists in nation building, and will also make our Parliamentarians, administrators, economists and the people at large more keenly aware that science and technology are a major national resource.*

Rajiv Gandhi, during his dynamic years, took new initiatives and made all efforts of employing science and technology for the building of a strong, vibrant and modern India of the 21st century. He believed in the role of science and technology towards the economic development of the society. He came with a mission to usher in a new technological era in the country.

A perusal of his collection of speeches on science and technology, including electronics and telecommunication, environment, agriculture, industrial development, technology innovation etc., delivered at many national and international fora, has clearly brought out his thought process, priorities and new action plan of modernizing India with the current developments of science and technology. According to Mrs. Sonia Gandhi * –

> *"His speeches and conversations, many of which have been published in five volumes of the Publications Division, reflect the breadth of his interests and the depth of his concerns. They outline his vision for the future of India and the world, his approach to their myriad problems and his potential philosophy. His words are a bacon of hope and a symbol of his tireless striving for solutions. They recount his struggles and his achievements. Above all, they reflect his dedication to his work and his country.*
>
> *This volume of extracts from hundreds of his speeches only provide a glimpse of the totality of Rajiv Gandhi's thoughts, actions and beliefs ... what he meant to India".*

* Foreword, Quotes of Rajiv Gandhi – Jagmohan Singh Raju, UBSPD, Delhi, 1994.

He took a different and positive stand, hitherto unknown, on the issues concerning the new development of science and technology in India, in relation to the needs and aspiration of the society and global progress. Rajiv Gandhi while inaugurating the 39th meeting of the National Development Council on Education Policy, in New Delhi, categorically said - *The idea today is not to eliminate or destroy the system that has been in practice. The attempt is to modify and guide the system, in particular specific directions and to try and stop any drift.*

The long road to implementation is now before us. This calls for partnership between science and Government. We have initiated steps to bring about changes in the administrative patterns and personal policies of institutions and departments manned by scientists and technologists. We are also trying to infuse a greater science – consciousness in to the decision – making process of Government as a whole. Government's economic and social policies have a direct bearing even on the utilization of available technologies, to say nothing of the development of new technologies especially suited to our needs and conditions.

Scientific activities should accelerate the pace of social change in the country. With his new imaginative, innovative and modern approach – Rajiv Gandhi initiated several new projects and programmes for harnessing the application of science and technology towards creating employment opportunities, as well as, for providing good quality of life to the people – the details of which are given in the subsequent sub - chapters here. He frankly expressed himself:

(Please see page numbers 66 to 242.)

3.1 Management of Science

Rajiv Gandhi's attitude towards the subject of Government administration was a little more critical. He said – "The problem in the development of our science and technology has been very much managerial. ..... This is an area that we would like to straighten out, clean up and speed up as much as possible. You (scientists) have to tell us what to do. And, I have found that our bureaucracy is very good in the areas in which they have been trained. But once you get out of that area into specialised areas, then you get terribly bogged down. Science and technology is one such area and we have to see how we can speed things up and rationlise them.... We have a very substantial scientific and technological base. We have to look ahead to see how India which is at a turning point will develop."[1] He said -

> *Our scientific and technological institutions some how do not allow young minds to come out to the fore. There is an administrative or may be a bureaucratic block and somehow this has to be overcome if we are to really progress.*
>
> *One thing is very clear – that at the rate at which science and technology is advancing, delay of even one or two generations of graduation may be too much of a gap to be able to be able to be in touch with the latest technology. I was talking with some Indians who handle very high sophisticated technology in advanced communications in the USA, and they are saying that once a man is over 35, he is just not in touch with the front line technology and he has to be moved out of basic research and design and to some other fields so that new minds can come in this direction, i.e., I don't say that we will be so drastic here.*
>
> *But the thinking has to be in this direction. We have to bring dynamism and movement in our more senior institutions.*

> *Perhaps managing science, is a problem and we really need to think more about how we are going to handle the management of science. Too often, the press seems to think management means getting somebody from the private sector who can manage everything. But it is not as simple as that: it is something that we have got to develop, we have got to think. Management means everything from the vision to the thinking to the actual implementation. It is not just getting a production line going.*[2]

"One of the problems in India has been with our scientists salary, their facilities, their perks, even more important, what recognition they get, what special standing they get. And these are areas that we must somehow come face to face with and sort out. Social recognition is perhaps one of the most difficult areas to be talked about. He further said,- whether it is a question of broadcasting or telecommunication for better administration, for productivity or better assessment of markets for the farmers, whether it is better weather information to help the farmer sow his seeds or help the farmer protect his crop, *it is all technology working for the poor people in our country*. This is what technology is doing to the lives of our people. It is giving them a better quality of life."[3] This was his free, frank and genuine feelings.

On the question of monitoring and evaluation of projects i.e., redeployment of resources, re-examining of priorities, achievement of targets or just cancelling a project, he said –

> *This really means that what we are looking for is much better Scientific Administration. Scientific administration must be a subject of its own. It cannot be borrowed from general bureaucratic system because it is not going to work. At the same time the answer is not to find the best scientist we have got and put him in charge as an administrator because then we lose a scientist. Perhaps we do not even gain in administration. It is a very specialized task: we have not developed people in this area and we must see*

how we can develop this. Again, this is an area you could debate and see what are the qualities that are needed, what sort of training and direction are required to produce this cadre of people, who would really support our scientists and our laboratories. It is only when we are able to work in this manner that we will be striving for world leadership in a number of fields.

The real question which we are facing in science, in technology, in research and generally across the board is that of management. How are we going to handle our scientific management? This perhaps is the root of getting more output from our scientists.[4]

Pandit Nehru, addressing the Indian Science Congress Association, 1963, had said –

> ***Our laboratories have done work and yet I have a feeling that all is not quite well with these labs.*** *Perhaps I (Rajiv Gandhi) could repeat that today. Questions of seniority, questions of bureaucracy coming into scientific management, of mediocrity creeping in at the higher administrative level and many other such questions have to be answered. They cannot be answered by us, they must be answered by you scientists. The only real way to get our best scientists operational in their fields is to refuse to accept mediocrity at any level. And this is the real challenge that our scientists must take on their own.*
>
> *...I think amongst the top countries in the number of papers that our scientists produce. But how many of these papers are quoted by other scientists? How many are referred to by others? Do we ever hear of these papers some years later or do they just disappear? This is a question that we must put and we must see that what we produce is really a top-grade frontline stuff. We have the capability. We have*

demonstrated it. We must bring them out and let them flower in a similar manner in every field.

Rajiv Gandhi wanted the basic attitudinal changes in the Government. He said:

Our over-riding priority is the removal of poverty, the war on poverty. Mr. Chief Minister, you have very rightly asked the question why are we so poor while we have such brilliant scientists and such brilliant research. While I shall leave it to you to find an answer to that, I could perhaps just say a few words. One reason, I am sure, that we from the Government do not chase our scientists to give us the answers that we are looking for. Instead we chase the bureaucracy. We must chase the scientists for our answers. We must not get off their backs till they give us the answers.

You mentioned a case in point – water reserves. I know what it has been like chasing all the state governments, talking to them, "Look, here are the maps, for heaven's sake use them". We have got to reverse this.

We have to get the Government coming to the scientific departments and saying – "Look, these are our problems, we want answers. You give us the answers". Well, it is when this basic attitude changes in the Government that our scientists will be giving us the results that we are asking for.[5]

It is universally accepted that science and technology are extremely vital for any country. Investment in science and technology is directly proportional to the rate of emergence of a nation as a global economic and political power. Rajiv Gandhi said -

Development and science are inter-related. Underdevelopment, by definition, is the lack of being able to use modern science and technology for the benefit of our people to increase their productivity, to increase their comforts, to improve their life span. If we are going to break this barrier, it must come from scientific institutions and our scientists, technologists and industrialists.

Even today, if we try to assess the difference between developed countries and others, there is, in reality, only one criterion – what is the level of technology in use among the common people. The lower the level, the greater their backwardness. The higher the level, the greater the development, the more their progress, the more the improvement in their lives. We have to assess the extent of technology's role in their daily life. Without science and technology, nothing can be achieved. Today, we have to understand that science is not something esoteric, it is the common man's helper to assist and transform our lives.

Rajiv Gandhi adopted a Technology Mission approach to put science into action, in the service of society. He said at the Lal Bahadur Shastri Award giving ceremony on 13 February 1989, that – *We have started several technology missions, each of which can transform our society. We have identified several areas, which appear to us important in today's India that need to be transformed. Drinking water, oilseeds, immunizing children against diseases, literacy, telecommunications and dairying – each one transforms the life of the common man. But this transformation can take place only when we make use of the best technology, the best science. Second – rate stuff adds to the costs, reduces the benefits. Much benefit can accrue to the farmers, especially in the areas of biotechnology. Again, in our space technology, the first remote sensing satellite we have set up renders direct assistance to the farmer. We can see where the water is under the ground and how much there is, how much can be taken out and when we should stop extracting more?*

When we installed our INSAT satellite, it told us about the rainfall. We have now purchased an excellent computer for the one specific purpose of helping the farmer to know when there will be rain so that he can sow his seeds at the proper time.

It is infact, the sipirit of science-administrators that matters in the management of science in the country.

References

1. Rajiv Gandhi - Conference on Science and Technology in India – Retrospect and Prospect, New Delhi, 13 November 1985.
2. — Silver Jubilee Convocation, Indian Institute of Technology, New Delhi, 19 December 1985.
3. —73rd Session of the Indian Science Congress Association, 8 January 1986, New Delhi.
4. — Conference of the Directors of National Laboratories, CSIR, New Delhi, 28 May 1986.
5. — 74th Session of the Indian Science Congress Association, Bangalore, 3 January 1987.

3.2 Brain-drain and Mediocrity

The problem of brain drain is an international one. Western Europe also loses able scientists, technicians and specialists to the United States and Canada. The migration is caused not only by the greater opportunities for specialized work which the more advanced countries offer, but in India by the lack of job opportunities in our country. Yet it is an absurd situation that a country like ours struggling with massive problems of development, should infact be rendering technical assistance through the import of brainpower to the advanced nations of the West. This question is of vital importance to us and we must devise ways and means of preventing this type of intellectual waste. This has not to be done by restrictions, legislation or executive fiat, but by providing more and more creative opportunities for scientists and other specialists in India said Rajiv Gandhi. He further stated that -

> *Advanced countries are lands of opportunity. They tend to attract the bright and the adventurous from other parts of the world. This inflow of talented manpower, in the form of trained doctors, technologists and scholars, could be called the contribution of the developing world to the welfare of the developed one.*
>
> *Brain drain, as it is popularly called, is a complex phenomenon. But it would be more appropriate to regard it as a form of human resource development, the process by which individuals acquire greater knowledge and experience. These skills will be available for the mother countries as well. Indian scientists, technologists, doctors and professionals who go abroad need not be thought of as a debit but as an investment.*
>
> *Many of them want to return, but find that working conditions back home will not provide outlets for all their skills, apart from the economic emoluments. Qualified persons also face problems in lateral entry because of resistance from those who are already*

> *established in the universities, research centers and industries. These are not insuperable problems. We are working out programmes and policies to help qualified Indian scientists and scholars who wish to return and work for the people of India.*
>
> *India teems in challenges. Using new knowledge for solving long-felt needs is itself a great adventure. The adventure demands the pooling of ideas and initiative, which will enable us to make better use of the energies of India's talented people, wherever they are.*
>
> *We have seen (during the last forty years of independence) that the principles and policies that had been enunciated and implemented by Gandhiji, Jawaharlal Nehru and Indiraji, were very much in the right direction and had strengthened and built our foundations. We have succeeded in developing our human resources and in developing a basic trained manpower and our mental resources in the country.*[1]

Rajiv Gandhi held the thesis that – "Mention has been made of brain drain. This is one of our major problems, but *I see it differently.* When one talks of brain- drain, one assumes that the phase of learning ends, as you get your degree; and that you have a developed brain, and now you are leaving the country; so it is brain drain. *But I do not agree with that all.* Learning continues right through life. It does not stop at any stage. If a few people go out, they are going to increase that learning. What we must see is that ultimately when further knowledge has been gained, further experience has been gained; these brains come back to our country again. If somebody does not come back at all, yes that is brain drain. But if somebody goes out when he is 23, or 25, or 30, I do not consider that brain-drain, provided we can get him back at a later date to use his further experience, his further knowledge, for the benefit of our country.

"We must produce the atmosphere, the infrastructure for it in industry, in our research establishments, in our academic institutions and we are attempting to do this. But in any developing country, this does take time.

"We in India are privileged that we are able to produce more such people. We are ahead on the human development side. We have produced more able people than we can use. It is a much better situation than having fewer people that are needed. The optimum would be if we could balance the two. But it takes a little while to do that." [2]

The Brain Bank – this was a new concept he introduced; he explained:

> *Another point, which has been talked about many times, is that of the brain drain, or as I prefer to call it,* ***the Brain – bank****. At the same time, if we are to stop brain – drain of too many scientists and technologists leaving the country, we have to tailor the subjects that we are teaching to the needs for our development. If we teach every one very esoteric subject which do not relate to the development in India, of course they will leave the country, they will go away and they will look for jobs elsewhere. So, we need in the exercise of the New Education Policy to first try and address what will be our needs of agricultural scientists, what will be our needs of technologists, of engineers, of other specialized training and then try to fit that back into the Education Policy. ...Unless this sort of training is done effectively, we will not be able to use the best resources in terms of brainpower in our country, for our development purposes.*[3]

He further demonstrated how this may be done: "If we are to utilize the brains that are unavailable in India, we must create an environment in which they can work. An environment which promotes mediocrity cannot be an environment in which excellence can flourish. We must change this mood which benefits non-achievers to a mood which really benefits the achievers and then we will be really able to move much faster. It is only then that Indians, manning very high positions in the forefront of technologies and research, will want to come back and help in our work, ... for the development of India, for our progress." He further said -

We can and are producing scientists who are equal to the best in the world. Sometimes it is evidenced by what is popularly known as the brain drain, with a lot of our scientists leaving the country. I myself prefer to look at it in a different perspective. I do not see the education process ending with graduation or ending at any particular time. I see it as continuing process of gaining knowledge throughout one's life by work, by research, by different inputs and in that idiom, I see the going out of scientists as only one more phase in gaining that knowledge provided we can get them back to work for us when we are ready to have that knowledge and employ that knowledge. And it is for us to create an environment where scientists start coming back.[4]

Rajiv Gandhi while accepting the Lenin Peace prize, on behalf of his mother, Mrs. Indira Gandhi, said in USSR, on 21 May 1985 that –

"In this vast undertaking of modernization, we have received invaluable understanding and cooperation from the Soviet Union. Your contribution has been particularly crucial to us in building up our mineral, metallurgical and machine building. ... As India's industry, science and technology grow, we shall need to have greater exchange with the Soviet Union and other great industrial countries. Our joint efforts will benefit both economies".

Rajiv Gandhi said in Rajya Sabha, on 17 December 1985 that –

Unless we are able to give science and technology in India, not just imported science and technology, but Indian science and technology a major thrust, we will not be able to keep up this self-suffiency that we have generated so far.

His words are evidence of great foresight as well as generosity of spirit. If other countries gained from our intelligentsia, we had no objection, but expressed the hope that our scientists would return enriched by their experience abroad. "Science has no political problems. It flows across all boundaries. Ideas, concepts and the consequences of various scientific endeavours are a common heritage for all humanity and it is therefore, for our scientists not be cocooned in the knowledge that is available with certain boundaries.

We must encourage our scientists to reach out for knowledge that is available elsewhere. We must assist them to interact with other scientists, especially in new areas of development. This is most essential for scientific development and cooperation with many countries and including the USA, the USSR, and this will broaden and perhaps equally help scientists of other countries. We must have much greater cross – fertilization of ideas of experience, of expertise. This is essential for fully realizing the scientific wealth and talent in our country."[5]

He further said -

> *In quantity, we say we have the third largest pool of manpower. But it is grossly bloated by mediocrity. And this must be cut out if our science and scientists are to compete. Last year we brought out a New Education Policy, which we feel will bring down many of these barriers. It will need the cooperation of the scientific community.*
>
> He wanted to remove mediocrity in the system. *He said – "The best scientists find it better to go into scientific development, into scientific research, we have got to change this. We have to change the basic thinking in our society. Development must relate to science and science must relate to development. It is only then, we shall be getting the answers, we shall get the development that we are looking for. Again, there is a very major political question involved. ... we must have the will to break this vested interest and weed out mediocrity,. In keeping the status quo, in keeping mediocrity alive, ... we stifle excellence. We do not allow it to grow.*

He was particularly anxious about shielding mediocrity. "We must be more careful about quality, especially in science and technology. There is no place for mediocrity in science and technology, because by definition, there cannot be – if you are going to protect mediocrity in any bureaucratic or other form. Then you are going to kill scientific development and high technology. We have to move out of this phase of a very bureaucratized scientific structure into much more dynamic structure where those who are really at the frontiers, those with good minds for science, for development and for the betterment of our country...we must work towards reducing this (mediocrity) and improving the percentage of excellence that is available."[6] He said -

> *We also need to orient our educational system in the direction of keeping up with the developments in science so that students and teachers are with a desire to be up-to-date with all that is contemporary and relevant. This will incidentally contribute to reducing professional frustration among the more talented of our scientists. Further, the mismatch between the scientific manpower we are generating and the manpower needs of our science will be repaired. It is indeed ironic that the country with the third largest reservoir of trained scientific ability nearly 4.4 million strong (data 1989) should be facing such an acute shortage in important areas of the kind of scientific talent required. In addition, by securing excellence through prioritization, we will be able to encash some of the resources we have built up in brain banks abroad among non-resident Indian students who would wish to return to their homeland enriched by the experience they have gained in other countries.* [7]

References

1. Rajiv Gandhi —Foundation laying Function of the Indian National Academy of Engineering, New Delhi, 11 April 1988.
2. — Silver Jubilee Convocation Address. Indian Institute of Technology, Delhi, 19 December 1985.
3. — Speech in Lok Sabha, 10 April 1986.
4. — Conference of Directors of the National Laboratories of the Council of Scientific and Industrial Research, New Delhi, 28 May 1986.
5. — Foundations Day Celebrations of the Council of Scientific and Industrial Research, CSIR, New Delhi, 26 September 1987.
6. — Speech in the Lok Sabha, 10 April 1986.
7. — 76th Session of the Indian Science Congress Association, Madurai, 3 January 1989.

National Policy on Education-1986

PART-I

INTRODUCTORY

1.1. Education has continued to evolve, diversify and extend its reach and coverage since the dawn of human history. Every country develops its system of education to express and promote its unique socio-cultural identity and also to meet the challenges of the times.There are moments in history when a new direction has to be given to an age-old process. That moment is today.

1.2. The country has reached a stage in its economic and technical development when a major effort must be made to derive the maximum benefit from the assets already created and to ensure that the fruits of change reach all sections. Education is the highway to that goal.

1.3. With this aim in view, the Government of India announced in January 1985 that a new Education Policy would be formulated for the country. A comprehensive appraisal of the existing educational scene was made, followed by a countrywide debate. The views and suggestions received from different quarters were carefully studied.

The 1968 Educatlon Policy and After

1.4. The National Policy of 1968 marked a significant step in the history of education in post-Independence India. It aimed to promote national progress, a sense of common citizenship and culture,' and to strengthen national integration. It laid stress on the need for a radical reconstruction of the education system, to improve its quality at all stages, and gave much greater attention to science and technology, the cultivation of moral values and a closer relation between education and the life of the people.

1.5. Since the adoption of the 1968 Policy, there has been considerable expansion in educational facilities all over the country at all levels. More than 90% of the country's rural habitations now have schooling facilities within a radius of one kilometer. There has been sizeable augmentation of facilities at other stages also.

1.6. Perhaps the most notable developnent has been the acceptance of a comnon structure of education throughout the country and the introduction of the 10+2+3 system by most states. In the school curricula, in addition to laying down a common scheme of studies for boys and girls, science and mathematics were incorporated. as compulsory subjects and work experience assigned a place of importance.

1.7. A beginning was also made in restructuring of courses at the undergraduate level. Centres of Advanced Studies were set up for post-graduate education and research. And we have been able to meet our requirements of educated manpower.

1.8. While these achievements are impressive by themselves, the general formulations incorporated in the 1968 Policy did not, however, get translated into a detailed strategy of implementation, accompanied by the assignment of specific responsibilities and financial and organisational support. As a result, problems of access, quality, quantity, utility and financial outlay, accumulated over the years, have now assumed such massive proportions that they must be tackled with the utmost urgency.

1.9. Education in India stands at the cross roads today. Neither normal linear expansion nor the existing pace and nature of improvement can meet the needs of the situation.

1.10. In the Indian way of thinking, a human being is a positive asset and a precious national resource which needs to be cherished, nurtured and developed with tenderness and care, coupled with dynamism. Each individual's growth presents a different range of problems. and requirements, at every stage from the womb to the tomb. The catalytic action of Education in this complex and dynamic growth process needs to be planned meticulously and executed with great sensitivity.

1.11. India's political and social life is passing through a phase which poses the danger of erosion to long-accepted values. The goals of secularism, socialism, democracy and professional ethics are coming under increasing strain.

1.12. The rural areas, with poor infrastructure and social services, will not get the benefit of trained and educated youth, unless rural-urban disparities are reduced and determined measures are taken to promote diversification and dispersal of employment opportunities.

1.13. The growth of our population needs to be brought down significantly over the coming decades. The largest single factor that could help achieve education among women.

1.14. Life in the coming decades is likely to bring new tensions together with unprecedented opportunities. To enable the people to benefit in the new environment will require new designs of human resource development. The coming generations should have the ability to internalise new ideas constantly and creatively. They have to be imbued with a strong commitment to humane values and to social justice. All this implies better education.

1 .15. Besides, a variety of new challenges and social needs make it imperative for the Government to formulate and implement a new Education Policy for the country. Nothing short of this will meet the situation.

PART II
THE ESSENCE AND ROLE OF EDUCATION

2.1. In our national perception education is essentially for all. This is fundamental to our all-round development, material and spiritual.

2.2. Education has an acculturating role.It refines sensitivities and perceptions that contribute cohesion, a scientific temper and independence spirit— thus furthering the goals of socialism,secularism and democracy enshrined in our Constitution.

2.3. Education develops manpower for different levels of the economy. It is also the substrate on which research and development flourish, being the ultimate guarantee of national self-reliance.

2.4. In sum, Education is a unique investment in the present and the future.This cardinal principle is the key National Policy on Education.

PART III
NATIONAL SYSTEM OF EDUCATION

3.1. The Constitution embodies the principles on which the National System of Education is conceived of.

3.2. The concept of a National System of Education implies up to a given level, all students, irrespective of caste, creed, location or sex, have access to education of a comparable quality. To achieve this, the goverment will initiate appropriately funded programmes.Effective measures will taken in the direction of the common school system recommended in the 1968 Policy.

3.3. The National System of Education envisages a common educational structure. The 10+2+3 structure has now been accepted in all parts of the country. Regarding the further break-up of the first 10 years efforts will be made to move towards an elementary system comprising 5 years of primary education and 3 years of upper primary, followed by 2 years of High School.

3.4. The National System of Education will be based on a national curricular framework which contains a common core along with other components that are flexible. The common core will include the history of India's freedom movement, the constitutional obligations and other content essential to nurture national identity. These elements will cut across subject areas and will be designed to promote values such as India's common cultural heritage, egalitarianism, democracy and secularism, equality of the sexes, protection of the environment, removal of social barriers observance of the small family norm and inculcation of the scientific temper. All educational programmes will be carried on in strict conformity with secular values.

3.5. India has always worked for peace and understanding between nations, treating the whole world as one family. True to this hoary tradition, Education has to strengthen this world view and motivate the younger generations for international cooperation and peaceful co-existence. This aspect cannot be neglected.

3.6. To promote equality, it will be necessary to provide for equal opportunity to all not only in access, but also in the conditions for success. Besides, awareness of the inherent equality of all will be created through the core curriculum. The purpose is to remove prejudices and complexes transmitted through the social environment and the accident of birth.

3.7. Minimum levels of learning will be laid down for such stage of education. Steps will also be taken to foster among students an understanding of the diverse cultural and social systems of the people living in different parts of the country. Besides the promotion of the link language, programmes will also be "launched to increase substantially the translation of books from one language to another and to publish multilingual dictionaries and glossaries. The young will be encouraged to undertake the rediscovery of India, each in his own image and perception.

3.8. In higher education in general, and technical education in particular, steps will be taken to facilitate inter-regional mobility by providing equal access to every Indian of requisite merit, regardless of his origins. The universal character of universities and other institutions of higher education is to be underscored.

3.9. In the areas of research and development and education in science and. technology, special measures will be taken to establish network arrangements between different institutions in the country to pool their resources and participate in projects of national importance.

3.10. The Nation as a whole will assume the responsibility of providing resource support for implementing programmes of educational transformation, reducing disparities, universalisation of elementary education, adult literacy scientific and technological research, etc.

3.11. Life-long education is a cherished goal of the educational process. This presupposes universal literacy. Opportunities will be provided to the youth, housewives, agricultural and industrial workers and professionals to continue the education of their choice, at the pace suited to them. The future thrust will be in the direction of open and distance learning.

3.12. The institutions which will be strengthened toplay an important role in giving shape to the National System of Education are the University Grants Commission, the All India Council of Technical Education, the Indian Council of Agricultural Research and the Indian Medical Council. Integrated planning will be instituted among all these bodies so as to establish functional linkages and reinforce programmes of research and postgraduate education. These, together with the National Council of Educational Research and Training, the National Institute of Educational Planning and Administration and the International Institute of Science and Technology Education will be involved in implementing the Education Policy.

A Meaningful Partnership

3.13. The Constitutional Amendment of 1976, which includes Education in the Concurrent List, was a far-reaching step whose implications—substantive, financial and administrative - require a new sharing of responsibility between the Union Government and the states in respect of this vital area of national life. While the role and responsibility of the states in regard to education will remain essentially unchanged, the Union Government would accept a larger responsibility to reinforce the national and integrative character of education, to maintain quality and standards (including those of the teaching profession at all levels), to study and monitor the educational requirements of the country as a whole in regard to manpower for developnent, to cater to the needs of research and advanced study, to look after the international aspects of education, culture and Human Resource Development and, in general, to promote excellence at all levels of the educational pyramid throughout the country. Concurrency signifies a partnership which is at once meaningful and challenging; the National Policy will be oriented towards give effect to it in letter and spirit.

PART IV
EDUCATION FOR EQUALITY

Disparities

4.1. The new Policy will lay special emphasis on the removal of disparities and to equalise educational opportunity by attending to the specific needs of those who have been denied equality so far.

Education for Women's Equality

4.2. Education will be used as an agent of basic change in the status of woman. In order to neutralise the accumulated distortions of the past, there will be a well-conceived edge in favour of women. The National Education System will play a positive, interventionist role in the empowerment of women. It will foster the development of new values through redesigned curricula, textbooks, the training and orientation of teachers, decision-makers and administrators, and the active involvement of educational institutions. This will be an act of faith and social engineering. Women's studies will be promoted as a part of various courses and educational institutions encouraged to take up active programmes to further women's development.

4.3. The removal of women's illiteracy and obstacles inhibiting their, access to, and retention in, elementary education will receive overriding priority, through provision of special support services, setting of time targets, and effective monitoring. Major emphasis will be laid on women's participation in vocational, technical and professional education at different levels. The policy of non-discrimination will be pursued vigorously to eliminate sex stereo-typing in vocational and professional courses and to promote women's participation in non-traditional occupations, as well as in existing and emergent technologies.

The Education of Scheduled Castes

4.4. The central focus in the SCs' educational development is their equalisation with the non-SC population at all stages and levels of education, in all areas and in all the four dimensions-rural male, rural female, urban male and urban female.

4.5. The measures contemplated for this purpose include:

(i) Incentives to indigent families to send their children to school regularly till they reach the age of 14.

(ii) Pre-matric Scholarship scheme for children of families engaged in occupations such as scavenging, flaying and tanning to be made applicable from Class I onwards. All children of such families, regardless of incomes, will be covered by this scheme and time-bound programmes targetted on them will be undertaken;

(iii) Constant micro-planning and verification to ensure that the enrolment, retention and successful completion of courses by SC students do not fall at any stage, and provision of remedial courses to improve their prospects for further education and employment.

(iv) Recruitment of teachers from Scheduled Castes;

(v) Provision of facilities for SC students in students' hostels at district headquarters, according to a phased programme;

(vi) Location of school buildings, Balwadis and Adult Education Centres in such a way as to facilitate full participation of the Scheduled Castes;

(vii) The utilization of N.R.E.P. and R.L.E.G.P. resources so as to make substantial educational facilities available to the Scheduled Castes; and

(viii) Constant innovation in finding new methods to ircrease the participation of the Scheduled Castes in the educational process.

The Education of Scheduled Tribes

4.6. The following measures will be taken urgently to bring the Scheduled Tribes on par with others:-

(i) Priority will be accorded to opening primary schools in tribal areas. The construction of school buildings will be undertaken in these areas on a priority basis under the normal funds for education, as well as under the N.R.E.P, R.L.E.G.P. Tribal Welfare schemes, etc.

(ii) The socio-cultural milieu of the STs has its distinctive characteristics including, in many cases, their own spoken languages. This underlines the need to develop the curricula and devise instructional materials in tribal languages at the initial stages, with arrangements for switching over to the regional language.

(iii) Educated and promising Scheduled Tribe youths will be encouraged and trained to take up teaching in tribal areas.

(iv) Residential schools, including Ashram Schools; will be established on a large scale.

(v) Incentive schemes will be formulated for the Scheduled Tribes, keeping in view their special needs and life styles. Scholarships for higher education will emphasise technical, professional and para-professional courses. Special remedial courses and other programmes to remove psycho-social impediments will be provided to improve their performance in various courses.

(vi) Anganwadis, Non-formal and Adult Education Centres will be opened on a priority basis in areas predominantly inhabited by the Scheduled Tribes.

(vii) The curriculum at all stages of education will be designed to create an awareness of the rich cultural identity of the tribal people as also of their enormous creative talent.

Other Educationally Backward Sections and Areas

4.7. Suitable incentives will be provided to all educationally backward sections of society, particularly in the rural areas. Hill and desert districts, remote and inaccessible areas and islands will be provided adequate institutional infrastructure.

Minorities

4.8. Some minority groups are educationally deprived or backward. Greater attention will be paid to the education of these groups in the interests of equality and social justice. This will naturally include the Constitutional guarantees given to them to establish and administer their own educational institutions, and protection to their languages and culture. Simultaneously, objectivity will be reflected in the preparation of textbooks and in all school activities, and all possible measures will be taken to promote an integration based on appreciation of common national goals and ideals, in conformity with the core curriculum.

The Handicapped

4.9. The objective should be to integrate the physically and mentally handicapped with the general community as equal partners, to prepare them for normal growth and to enable them to face life with courage and confidence. The following measures will be taken in this regard :

(i) Wherever it is feasible, the education of children with motor handicaps and other mild handicaps will be common with that of others.

(ii) Special schools with hostels will be provided, as far as possible at district headquarters, for the severely handicapped children.

(iii) Adequate arrangements will be made to give vocational training to the disabled.

(iv) Teachers training programmes will be reoriented, in particular for teacher of primary classes, to deal with the special difficulties of the handicapped children; and

(v) Voluntary effort for the education of the disabled, will be encouraged in every possible manner.

Adult Education

4.10. Our ancient scriptures define education as that which liberates - i.e. provides the instruments for liberation from ignorance and oppression. In the modern world, it would naturally include the ability to read and write, since that is the main instrument of learning. Hence the crucial importance of adult education, including adult literacy.

4.11. The critical developnent issue today is the continuous upgradation of skills so as to produce manpower resources of the kind and the number required by the society. Since participion by beneficiaries in the developmental programmes is of crucial importance, systematic programmes of adult education linked with national goals such as alleviation of poverty, national integration, environmental conservation, energisation of the cultural creativity of the people, observance of small norm, promotion of women's equality, etc. will be organised and the existing programmes reviewed and strengthened.

4.12. The whole Nation must pledge itself to the eradication of illiteracy, particularly in the 15-35 age group. The Central and State Governments, political parties and their mass organisations, the mass media and educational institutions must commit themselves to mass literacy programmes of diverse nature. It will also have to involve on a large scale teachers, students, youth, voluntary agencies, employers, etc. Concerted efforts will be made to harness various research agencies to improve the pedagogical aspects of adult literacy. The mass literacy programme would include, in addition to literacy, functional knowledge and skills, and also awareness among learners about the socil-economic reality and the possibility to change it.

4.13. A vast programme of adult and continuing education will be implemented, through various ways and channels, including-

(a) establishment of centres in rural areas for continuing education;

(b) workers' education through the employers, unions and concerned agencies of government;

(c) post-secondary education institutions;

(d) wider promotion of books, libraries and reading rooms, use of radio, TV and films, as mass and group learning media;

(e) creation of learners' groups and organisations;

(f) programmes of distance learning;

(g) organizing assistance in self-learning; and

(h) organising need and interest based vocational training programmes.

PART V
REORGANISATION OF EDUCATION AT DIFFERENT STAGES

Early Childhood Care and Education

5.1. The National Policy on Children specially emphasises investment in the development of the young child, particularly children from sections of the population in which first generation learners predominate.

5.2. Recognising the holistic nature of child developnent, viz., nutrition, health and social, mental, physical, moral and emotional development, Early Childhood Care and Education (ECCE) will receive high priority and be suitably integrated with the Integrated Child Development Services programme, wherever possible. Day-care centres will be provided as a support service for universalisation of primary education, to enable girls engaged in taking care of siblings to attend school and as a support service for working women belonging to poorer sections.

5.3. Programmes of ECCE will be child-oriented, focussed around play and the individuality of the child. Formal methods and introduction of the 3 R's will be discouraged at this stage. The local community will be fully involved in these programmes.

5.4. A full integration of childcare and pre-primary education will be brought about, both as a feeder and a strengthening factor for primary education and for human resources development in general. In continuation this stage, the school of Health Programme will be strengthened.

Elementary Education

5.5. The new thrust in elementary education will emphasise two aspects. : (i) universal enrolment and universal retention of children up to 14 years of age, and (ii) a substantial improvement in the quality of education.

Child-centred Approach

5.6. A warm, welcoming and encouraging approach, in which all concerned share a solicitude for the needs of the child, is the best motivation for the child to attend school and learn. A child-centred and activity-based process of learning should be adopted at the primary stage. First generation learners should be allowed to set their own pace and be given supplementary remedial instruction. As the child grows, the component of cognitive learning will be increased and skills, organised through practice. The policy of non-detention at the primary stage will be retained, making evaluation as disaggregated as feasible. Corporal punishment will be firmly excluded from the educational system and school timings as well as vacations adjusted to the convenience of children.

School Facilities

5.7. Provision will be made of essential facilities in primary schools, including at least two reasonably large rooms that are usable in all weather, and the necessary toys, blackboards, maps, charts, and other leading material. At least two teachers, one of whom a woman, should work in every school, the number increasing as early as possible to one teacher per class. A phased drive, symbolically called OPERATION BLACKBOARD will be undertaken with immediate effect to improve Primary Schools all over the country. Government, local bodies, voluntary agencies and individuals will be fully involved. Construction of school buildings will be the first charge on NREP and RLEGP funds.

Non-formal Education

5.8. A large and systematic programme of non-formal education will be launched for school drop-outs, for children from habitations without schools, working children and girls who cannot attend whole-day schools.

5.9. Modern technological aids will be used to improve the learning environment of NFE centres. Talented and dedicated young men and women from the local community will be chosen to serve as instructors, and particular attention paid to their training. Steps will be taken to facilitate their entry into the formal system in deserving cases. All necessary measures will be taken to ensure that the quality of non-formal education is comparable with formal education.

5.10. Effective steps will be taken to provide a framework for the curriculum on.the lines of the national core curriculum, but based on the needs of the learners and related to the local environment. Learning material of high quality will be developed and provided free of charge to all pupils. NFE programmes will provide participatory learning environment, and activities such as games and sports, cultural programmes, excursions, etc.

5.11. Much of the work of running NFE centres will be done through voluntary agencies and panchayati raj institutions. The provision of funds to these agencies will be adequate and timely. The Government will take over-all responsibility for this vital sector.

A Resolve

5.12. The New Education Policy will give the highest priority to solving the problem of children dropping out of school and will adopt an array of meticulously formulated strategies based on micro-planning, and applied at the grass-roots level all over the country, to ensure children's retention at school. This effort will be fully coordinated with the network of non-formal education. It shall be ensured that all children who attain the age of about 11 years by 1990 will have had five years of schooling, or its equivalent through the non-formal stream. Likewise, by 1995 all children will be provided free and compulsory education upto 14 years of age.

Secondary Education

5.13. Secondary education begins to expose students to the differentiated roles of science, the humanities and social sciences. This is also an appropriate stage to provide children with a sense of history and national perspective and give them opportunities to understand their constitutional duties and rights as citizens. Conscious internalisation of a healthy work ethos and of the values of a humane and composite culture' will be brought about through appropriately formulated curricula. Vocationalisation through specialised institutions or through the refashioning of secondary education can, at this stage, provide valuable manpower for economic growth. Access to secondary education will be widened to cover areas unserved by it at present. In other areas, the main emphasis will be on consolidation.

Pace-setting Schools

5.14. It is universally accepted that children with special talent or aptitude should be provided opportunities to proceed at a faster pace, by making good quality education available to them, irrespective of their capacity to pay for it.

5.15. Pace-setting schools intended to serve this purpose will be established in various parts of the country on a given pattern, but with full scope for innovation and experimentation. Their broad aims will be to serve the objective of excellence, coupled with equity and social justice (with reservation for SCs and STs), to promote national integration by providing opportunities to talented children largely rural, from different parts of the country to live and learn together, to develop their full potential, and, most importantly, to become catalysts of a nation-wide programme of school improvement. The schools will be residential and free of charge.

Vocationalisation

5.16. The introduction of systematic, well-planned and rigorously implemented programmes of vocational education is crucial in the proposed educational reorganisation. These elements are meant to enhance individual employability, to reduce the mis-match between the demand and supply of skilled manpower, and to provide an alternative for those pursuing higher education without particular interest or purpose.

5.17. Vocational education will be a distinct stream, intended to prepare students for identified occupations spanning several areas of activity. These courses will ordinarily be provided after the secondary stage, but keeping the scheme flexible, they may also be made available after Class VIII. In the interests of integrating vocational education better with their facilities the Industrial Training Institutes will also conform to the larger vocational pattern.

5.18. Health planning and health service management should optimally interlock with the education and training of appropriate categories of health manpower through health-related vocational courses. Health education at the primary and middle levels will ensure the commitment of the individual to family and community health, and lead to health-related vocational courses at the +2 stage of higher secondary education. Efforts will be made to devise similar vocational courses based on Agriculture, Marketing, Social Services, etc. An emphasis in vocational education will also be on development of attitudes, knowledge, and skills for entrepreneurship and self-employment.

5.19. The establishment of vocational courses or institutions will be the responsibility of the Government as well as employers in the public and private sectors; the Government will, however, take special steps to cater to the needs of women, rural and tribal students and the, deprived sections of society. Appropriate programmes will also be started for the handicapped.

5.20. Graduates of vocational courses will be given opportunities, under predetermined conditions, for professional growth, career improvement and lateral entry into courses of general, technical and professional education through appropriate bridge courses.

5.21. Non-formal, flexible and need-based vocational programnes will also be made available to neoliterates, youth who have completed primay education, school drop-outs, persons engaged in work and unemployed or partially employed persons. Special attention in this regard will be given to women.

5.22. Tertiary level courses will be organised for the young who graduate from the higher secondary courses of the academic stream and may also require vocational courses.

5.23. It is proposed that vocational courses cover 10 per cent of higher secondary students by 1990 and 25 per cent by 1995, Steps will be taken to see that a substantial majority of the products of vocational courses are employed or become self-employed. Review of the courses offered would be regularly undertaken. Government will also review its recruitment policy to encourage diversification at the secondary level.

Higher Education

5.24. Higher education provides people with an opportunity to reflect on the critical social, economic, cultural, moral and spiritual issues facing humanity. It contributes to national development through dissemination of specialized knowledge and skills. It is therefore a crucial factor for survival. Being at the apex of the educational pyramid, it has also a key role in producing teachers, for the 'education system.

5.25. In the context of the unprecedented explosion of knowledge, higher education has to become dynamic, as never before, constantly entering uncharted areas.

5.26. There are around 150 universities and about 5,000 colleges in India today. In view of the need to effect an all round improvenent in these institutions, it is proposed that, in the near future, the main emphasis will be on the consolidation of, and expansion of facilities in, the existing institutions.

5.27. Urgent steps degradation will be taken to protect the system from degradation

5.28. In view of mixed experiences with the system of affiliation, autonomous colleges will be helped to develop in large numbers until the affiliating system is replaced by a freer and more creative association of universities with colleges. Similarly, the creation of autonomous departments within universities on a selective basis will be encouraged. Autonomy and freedom will be accompanied by accountability.

5.29. Courses and programmes will be redesigned to meet the demands of specialisation better. Special emphasis will be laid on linguistic competence. There will be increasing flexibility in the combination of courses.

5.30. State level planning and coordination of higher education will be done through Councils of Higher Education. The UGC and these Councils will develop coordinative methods to keep a watch on standards.

5.31. Provision will be made for minimum facilities and admission will be regulated according to capacity. A major effort will be directed towards the transformation of teaching methods. Audio-visual aids and electronic equipment will be introduced; development of science and technology curricula and material, research, and teacher orientation will receive attention. This will require preparation of teachers at the beginning of the service as well as continuing education thereafter. Teachers' performance will be systematically assessed. All posts will be filled on the basis of merit.

5.32. Research in the universities will be provided enhanced support and steps will be taken to ensure its high quality. Suitable mechanisms will be set up by the UGC for coordinating research in the universities, particularly in thrust areas of science and technology, with research undertaken by other agencies. An effort will be made to encourage the setting up of national research facilities within the university system, with proper forms of autonomous management.

5.33. Research in Indology, the humanities and social sciences will receive adequate support. To fulfil the need for the synthesis of knowledge, inter-disciplinary research will be encouraged. Efforts will be made to delve into India's ancient fund of knowledge and to relate it to contemporary reality. This effort will imply the development of facilities for the intensive study of Sanskrit and other Classical languages.

5.34. In the interest of greater coordination and consistency in policy, sharing of facilities and developing inter-disciplinary research, a national body covering higher education in general, agricultural , medical, technical, legal and other professional fields will be set up.

Open University and Distance Learning

5.35. The Open University system has been initiated in order to augment opportunities for higher education and as an instrument of democratising education.

5.36. The Indira Gandhi National Open University, established in 1985 in fulfilment of these objectives, will be strengthened.

5.37. This powerful instrument will have to be developed with care and extended with caution.

Delinking Degrees from Jobs

5.38. A beginning will be made in de-linking degrees from jobs in selected areas.

5.39. The proposal cannot be applied to occupation-specific courses like Engineering, Medicine, Law, Teaching, etc. Similarly, the services of specialists with academic qualifications in the humanities, social sciences, sciences, etc. will continue to be required in various job positions.

5.40. De-linking will be applied in services for which a university degree need not be a necessary qualification. Its implementation will lead to a re-fashioning of job-specific courses and afford 'greater justice to those candidates who, despite being equipped for a given job, are unable to get it because of an unnecessary preference for graduate candidates.

5.41. Concomitant with de-linking, an appropriate machinery, such as a National Testing Service, will be established, in appropriate phases, to conduct tests on a voluntary basis to determine the suitability of candidates for specified jobs and to pave the way for the emergence of norms of comparable competence across the nation.

Rural University

5.42. The new pattern of the Rural University will be consolidated and developed on the lines of Mahatma Gandhi's revolutionary ideas on education so as to take up the challenges of micro-planning at grassroot levels for the transformation of rural areas. Institutions and programmes of Gandhian basic education will be supported.

PART VI
TECHNICAL AND MANAGEMENT EDUCATION

6. 1. Although the two streams of technical and management education are functioning separately, it is essential to look at them together, in view of their close relationship and complementary concerns. The reorganisation of Technical and Management Education should take into account the anticipated scenario by the turn of the century, with specific reference to the likely changes in the economy, social environment, production and management processes, the rapid expansion of knowledge and the great advances in science and technology.

6.2. The infrastructure and services sectors as well as the unorganised rural sector also need a greater induction of improved technologies and a supply of technical and managerial manpower. This will be attended' to by the Government.

6.3. In order to improve the situation regarding manpower information, the recently set up Technical Manpower Information System will be further developed and strengthened.

6.4. Continuing education,covering establised as well as emerging technologies, will be promoted.

6.5. As computers have become important and ubiguitous tools, a minimal exposure to computers and a training in their use will form part of professional education. Programmes of computer literacy will be organised on wide scale from the school stage.

6.6. In view of the present rigid entry requirements to formal courses restricting the access of a large segment of people to technical and managerial education, programmes through a distance-learning process, including use of the mass media, will be offered. Technical and management education programmes, including education in polytechnics, will also be on a flexible modular pattern based on credits, with provision for multi-point entry. A strong guidance and counselling service will be provided.

6.7. In order to increase the relevance of management education, particularly in the non-corporate and under-managed sectors, the management education system will study and document the Indian experience and create a body of knowledge and specific educational programmes suited to these sectors.

6.8. Appropriate formal and non-formal programmes of technical education, will be devised for the benefit of women, the economically and socially weaker sections, and the physically handicapped.

6.9. The emphasis on vocational education and its expansion will need a large number of teachers and professionals in vocational education, educational technology, curriculum development, etc. programmes will be started to meet this demand.

6.10. To encourage students to consider "self-employment" as a career option, training in entrepreneurship will be provided through modular or optional courses, in degree or diploma programmes.

6.11. In order to meet the continuing needs of updating curriculum, renewal should systematically phase out obsolescence and introduce new technologies or disciplines.

Institutional Thrusts

6.12 Some polytechnics in the rural areas have started training weaker groups in those areas for productive occupations.

through a system of community polytechnics. The community polytechnic system will be appraised and appropriately strengthened to increase its quality and coverage.

Innovation, Research and Development

6.13. Research as a means of renovation and renewal of educational processes will be undertaken by all higher technical institutions. It will primarily aim at producing quality manpower capable of taking up R&D functions. Research for development will focus on improving present technologies, developing new indigenous ones and enhancing production and productivity. A suitable system for watching and forecasting technology will be' set up.

6.14.The scope for cooperation, collaboration and networking relationships between institutions at various levels and with the user systems will be utilised. Proper maintenance, and an attitude of innovation and improvement will be promoted systematically.

Promoting Efficiency and Effectivness at all Levels

6.15. As technical and management education is expensive, the following major steps will be taken for cost-effectiveness and to promote excellence:

(i) High priority will be given to modernisation and removal of obsolescence. However, modernisation will be undertaken to enhance functional efficiency and not for its own sake or as a status symbol;

(ii) Institutions will be encouraged to generate resources using their capacities to provide services to the community and industry. They will be equipped with up-to-date learning resources, library and computer facilities;

(iii) Adequate hostel accommodation will be provided, specially for girls. Facilities for sports, creative work and cultural activities will be expanded:

(iv) More effective procedures will be adopted in the recruitment of staff. Career opportunities, service conditions, consultancy norms and other perquisites will be improved.

(v) Teachers will have multiple roles to perform; teaching, research, development of learning resources material, extension, and managing the institution. Initial and in-service training will be made mandatory for faculty members and adequate training reserves will be provided. Staff Development Programmes will be integrated at the State, and coordinated at Regional and National levels.

(vi) The curricula of technical and management programmes will be targetted on current as well as the projected needs of industry or user systems. Active interaction between technical or management institutions and industry will be promoted in programme planning and implementation, exchange of personnel, training facilities and resources, research and consultancy and other areas of mutual interest.

(vii) Excellence in performance of institutions and individuals will be recognised and rewarded. The emergence of substandard and institutions will be checked. A climate conducive to excellence and innovation will be promoted with full involvement of the faculty.

(viii) Select institutions will be awarded academic, administrative and financial autonomy of varying degrees, building in safeguards with respect to accountability.

(ix) Networking systems will have to be established between technical education and industry, R&D organisations, programmes of rural and community development, and with other sectors of education with complementary characteristics.

Management Functions and Change

6.16. In view of the likely emergence of changes in management systems and the need to equip students with the ability to cope with them, effective mechanisms will be devised to understand the nature and direction of change per se and to develop the important skill of managing change.

6.17. In view of the integrated nature of the task the Ministry of Human Resource Development will coordinate the balanced development of engineering, vocational and management education as well as the education of technicians and craftsmen.

6.18. Professional societies will be encouraged and enabled to perform their due role in the advancement of technical and management education.

6.19. The All India Council for Technical Education will be vested with statutory authority for planning, formulation and the maintenance of norms and standards, accreditation, funding of priority areas, monitoring and evaluation, maintaining parity of certification and awards and ensuring the coordinated and integrated development of technical and management education. Mandatory periodic evaluation will be carried out by a duly constituted Accreditation Board.

6.20. In the interests of maintaining standards and for several other valid reasons, the commercialisation of technical and professional education will be curbed. An alternative system will be devised to involve private and voluntary effort in this sector of education, in conformity with accepted norms and goals.

PART VII
MAKING THE SYSTEM WORK

7.1. It is obvious that these and many other new tasks of education cannot be performed in a state of disorder. Education needs to be managed in an atmosphere of utmost intellectual rigour, seriousness of purpose and, at the same time, of freedom essential for innovation and creativity. While far-reaching changes will have to be incorporated in the quality and range of education, the process of introducing discipline into the system will have to be started, here and now, in what exists.

7.2. The country has placed boundless trust in the educational system. The people have a right to expect concrete results. The first task is to make it work. All teachers should teach and all students study.

7.3. The strategy in this behalf will consist of -

(a) a better deal to teachers with accountability;
(b) provision of improved students services and insistence on observance of acceptable norms of behaviour;
(c) provision of better facilities to institutions; and
(d) creation of a system of performance appraisals of institutions according to standards and norms set at National or State levels.

PART VIII
REORIENTING THE CONTENT AND PROCESS OF EDUCATION

The Cultrual Perspective

8.1. The existing schism between the formal system of education and the country's rich and varied cultural traditions needs to be bridged. The preoccupation with modern technologies cannot be allowed to sever our new generations from the roots in India's history and culture. De-culturisation, de-humanisation and alienation must be avoided at all costs. Education can and bring about the fine synthesis between change-oriented technologies and the country's continuity' of cultural tradition.

8.2. The curricula and processes of education will be enriched by cultural content in as many manifestations as possible. Children will be enabled to develop sensitivity to beauty, harmony and refinement. Resource persons in the community, irrespective of their formal educational qualifications, will be invited to contribute to the cultural enrichment *of* education, employing both the literate and oral traditions of communication. To sustain and carry forward the cultural tradition, the role *of* old masters, who train pupils through traditional modes will be supported and recognised.

8.3. Linkages will be established between the university system and institutions of higher learning in art, archaeology, oriental studies etc. Due attention will also be paid to the specialised disciplines of Fine Arts, Museology, Folklore etc. Teaching, training and research in these disciplines will be strengthened so as to replenish specialised manpower in them.

Value Education

8.4. The growing concern over the erosion of essential values and an increasing cynicism in society has brought to focus the need for readjustments in the curriculum in order to take education a forceful tool for the cultivation of social and moral values.

8.5. In our culturally plural society, education should foster universal and eternal values, oriented towards the unity and integration of our people. Such value education should help eliminate obscurantism, religious fanaticism, violence, superstition and fatalism.

8.6. Apart from this combative role, value education has a profound positive content, based on our heritage, national goals universal perceptions. It should lay primary emphasis on this aspect.

Language

8.7. The Education Policy of 1968 had examined the question of the development of languages in great details; its essential provisions can hardly be improved upon and are as relevant today as before. The implementation of this part of the 1968 Policy has, however, been uneven. The Policy will be implemented more energetically and purposefully.

Books and Libraries

8.8. The availability of books at low prices is indispensable for people's education. Effort will be made to secure easy accessibility to books for all segments of the population. Measures will be taken to improve the quality of books, promote the 'reading habit and encourage creative writing. Authors interests will be protected. Good translations of foreign books into Indian languages will be supported. Special attention will be paid to the production of quality books for children, including text books and work books.

8.9. Together with the developnent of books, a nation-wide movement for the improvement of existing libraries and the establishment of new ones will be taken up. Provision will be made in all educational institutions for library facilities and the status of librarians improved.

Media and Educational Technology

8.10. Modern communication technologies have the potential to bypass several stages and sequences in the process of developnent encountered in earlier decades. Both the constraints of time and distance at once become manageable. In order to avoid structural dualism, modern educational technology must reach out to the most distant areas am the most deprived sections of beneficiaries simultaneously with the areas of comparative affluence and ready availability.

8.11. Educational technology will be employed in the spread of useful information, the training and re-training of teachers, to improve quality, sharpen awareness of art and culture, inculcate abiding values, etc., both in the formal and non-formal sectors. Maximum use will be made of the available infrastructure. In villages without electricity, batteries or solar packs will be used to run the programme.

8.12. The generation of relevant and culturally compatible educational programmes will form an important component of educational, technology and all available resources in the country will be utilised for this purpose.

8.13. The media have a profound influence on the minds of children as well as adults; some of them tend to encourage consumerism, violence etc. and have a deleterious effect. Radio and T.V. programmes which clearly militate against proper educational objectives will be prevented. Steps will be taken to discourage such trends in films and other media also. An active movement will be started to promote the production of childrens films of high quality and usefulness.

Work Experience

8.14. Work experience, viewed as purposive and meaningful manual work, organised as an integral part of the learning process and resulting in either goods or services useful to the community, is considered as an essential component at all stages of education, to be provided through well-structured and graded programmes. It would comprise activities in accord with the interests, abilities and needs of students, the level of skills and knowledge to be upgraded with the stages of education. This exprience would be helpful on his entry into the workforce. Pre-vocational programmes provided at the lower secondary stage will also facilitate the choice of the vocational courses at the higher secondary stage.

Education and Environment

8.15. There is a paramount need to create a consciousness of the environment. It must permeate all ages and all sections of society, beginning with the child. Environmental consciousness should inform teaching in schools and colleges. This aspect will be integrated in the entire educational process.

Mathematics Teaching

8.16. Mathematics should be visualised as the vehicle to train a child to think, reason, analyse and to articulate logically. Apart from being a specific subject, it should be treated as a concomitant to any subject involving analysis and reasoning.

8.17. With the recent introduction of computers in schools, educational computing and the emergence of learning through the understanding of cause-effect relationships and the interplay of variables, the teaching of mathematics will be suitably redesigned to bring it in line with modern technological devices.

Science Education

8.18. Science education will be strengthened so as to develop in the child well defined abilities and values such as the spirit of inquiry, creativity, objectivity, the courage to question, and an aesthetic sensibility.

8.19. Science education programmes will be designed to enable the learner to acquire problem solving and decision making skills and to discover the relationship of science with health, agriculture, industry and other aspects of daily life. Every effort will be made to extend science education to the vast numbers who have remained outside the pale of formal education.

Sports and Physical Education

8.20. Sports and physical education are an integral part of the learning process, and will be included in the evaluation of performance. A nation-wide infrastructure for physical education, sports and games will be built into the educational edifice.

8.21. The infrastructure will consist of playfields, equipment, coaches and teachers of physical education as part of the School Improvement Programme. Available open spaces in urban areas will be reserved for playgrounds, if necessary by legislation. Efforts will be made to establish sports institutions and hostels where specialised attention will be given to sports activities and sports-related studies, along with normal education. Appropriate encouragement will be given to those talented in sports and games. Due stress will be laid on indigenous traditional games. As a system which promotes an integrated development of body and mind, Yoga will receive special attention. Efforts will be made to introduce yoga in all schools; to this end, it will be introduced in teacher training courses.

The Role of Youth

8.22. Opportunities will be provided for the youth to involve themselves in national and social development through educational institutions and outside them. Students will be required to participate in one or the other of existing schemes, namely, the National Service Scheme, National Cadet Corps, etc. Outside the institutions, the youth will be encouraged to take up programmes of developnent, reform and extension. The National Service Volunteer Scheme will be strengthened.

The Evaluation Process and Examination Reform

8.23. Assessment of performance is an integral part of any process of learning and teaching. As part of sound educational strategy, examinations should be employed to bring about qualitative improvements in education.

8.24. The objective will be to re-cast the examination system so as to ensure a method of assessment that is a valid and reliable measure of student development and a powerful instrument for improving teaching and learning. In functional terms, this would mean:

- (i) The elimination of excessive element of chance and subjectivity;
- (ii) The de-emphasis of memorisation;
- (iii) Continuous and comprehensive evaluation that incorporates both scholastic and non-scholastic aspects of education, spread over the total span of instructional time;
- (iv) Effective use of the evaluation process by teachers,students and parents;
- (v) Improvement in the conduct of examinations;
- (vi) The introduction of concomitant changes in instructional materials and methodology;
- (vii) Introduction of the semester system from the secondary stage in a phased manner; and
- (viii) The use of grades in place of marks.

8.25. The above goals are relevant both for external examinations and evaluation within educational institutions. Evaluation at the institutional level will be streamlined and the predominance of external examinations reduced.

PART IX
THE TEACHER

9.1. The status of the teacher reflects the socio-cultural ethos of a society; it is said that no people can rise above the level of its teachers. The Government and the community should endeavour to create conditions which will help motivate and inspire teachers on constructive and creative lines. Teachers' should have the freedom to innovate, to devise appropriate methods of communication and activities relevant to the needs and capabilities of and the concerns of the community.

9.2. The methods of recruiting teachers will be reorganised to ensure merit, objectivity and conformity with spatial and functional requirements. The pay and service conditions of teachers have to be commensurate with their social and professional responsibilities and with the need to attract talent to the profession. Efforts will be made to reach the desirable objective of uniform emoluments, service conditions and grievance-removal mechanisms for teachers throughout the country. Guidelines will be formulated to ensure objectivity in the postings and transfers of teachers. A system of teacher evaluation-open, participative and data-based— will be createed and reasonable opportunities of promotion to higher grades provided. Norms of accountability will be laid down with incentives for good performance and disincentives for non-performance. Teachers will continue to play a crucial role in the formulation and implementation of educational programmes.

9.3. Teachers' associations must play a significant role in upholding professional integrity, enhancing the dignity of the teacher and in curbing professional misconduct. National level associations of teachers, could prepare a Code of Professional Ethics for Teachers and see to its observance

Teacher Education

9.4. Teacher education is a continuous process, and its pre-service and in-service components are inseparable. As the first step, the system of teacher education will be overhauled.

9.5. The new programmes of teacher-education will ernphasise continuing education and the need for teachers to meet the thrusts envisaged in this Policy.

9.6. District Institutes of Education and Training (DIET) will be established with the capability to organise pre-service and in-service courses for elementary school teachers and for the personnel working in non-formal and adult education. As DIETs get established, sub-standard institutions will be phased out. Selected Secondary Teacher Training Colleges will be upgraded to complement the work of State Councils of Educational Research and Training. The National Council of Teacher Education will be provided the necessary resources and capability to accredit institutions of teacher-education and provide guidance regarding curricula and methods. Networking arrangements will be created between institutions of teacher education and university departments of education.

PART X
THE MANAGEMENT OF EDUCATION

10.1 An overhaul of the system of planning and the management of education will receive high priority. The guiding considerations will be :-

(a) Evolving a long-term planning and management perspective of education and its integration with the Country's developmental and manpower needs;

(b) Decentralisation and the creation of a spirit of autonomy for educational institutions;

(c) Giving pre-eminence to people's involvement, including association of non-governnental agencies and voluntary effort;

(d) Inducting more women in the planning and management of education;

(e) Establishing the principle of accountability in relation to given objectives and norms.

National Level

10.2. The Central Advisory Board of Education will play a pivotal role in reviewing educational development, determining the changes required to improve the system and monitoring implementation. It will function through appropriate Committees and other mechanisms created to ensure contact with, and coordination among, the various areas of Human Resource Development. The Departments of Education at the Centre and in the States will be strengthened through the involvement of professionals.

Indian Education Service

10.3. A proper management structure in education will entail the establishment of the Indian Education Service as an All-India Service. It will bring a national perspective to this vital sector. The basic principles, functions and procedures of recruitment to this service will be decided in consultation with the State Governments.

State Level

10.4. State Governments may establish State Advisory Boards of Education on the lines of CABE. Effective measures should be taken to integrate mechanisms in the various State departments concerned with Human Resource Development.

10.5. Special attention will be paid to the training of educational planners, administrators and heads of institutions. Institutional arrangements for this purpose should be set up in stages.

District and Local Level

10.6. District Boards of Education will be created to manage education up to the higher secondary level. State Governments will attend to this aspect with all possible expedition within a multi-level framework of educational development, Central, State, District and Local level agencies will participate in planning, coordination, monitoring and evaluation.

10.7. A very important role must be assigned to the head of an educational institution. Heads will be specially selected and trained. School complexes will be promoted on a flexible pattern so as to serve as networks of institutions and synergic alliances to encourage professionalism among teachers, to ensure observance of norms of Conduct and to enable the sharing of experiences- and facilities. It is expected that a developed system of school complexes will take over much of the inspection functions in due course.

10.8. Local Communities through appropriate bodies, will be assigned a major role in programmes of school improvement.

Voluntary Agencies and Aided Instituions

10.9. Non-government and voluntary effort including social activist groups will be encouraged, subject to proper management, and financial assistance proovided. At the same time, steps will be taken to prevent the establishment of institution set up to commercialise education.

PART XI
RESOURCES AND REVIEW

11.1. The Education Commission of 1964-66, the National Education Policy of 1968 and practically all others concerned with education have stressed that the egalitarian goals and the practical development-oriented objectives of Indian society can be realised only by making investments in education of an order commensurate with the nature and dimensions of the task.

11.2. Resources, to the extent possible, will be raised by mobilising donations, asking the beneficiary communities to maintain school buildings and supplies of some consumables, raising fees at the higher levels of education and, effecting some savings by the efficient use of facilities. Institutions involved with research and the development of technical and scientific manpower should also mobilize some funds by levying a cess or charge on the user agencies, including Government departments, and entrepreneurs. All these measures will be taken not only to reduce the burden on State resources but also for creating a greater sense of responsibility within the educational system. However, such measures will contribute only marginally to the total funding. The Government and the community in general will find funds for such programmes as: the universalisation of elementary education; liquidating illiteracy; equality of access to educational opportunities to all sections throughout the country; enhancing the social relevance, quality and functional effectiveness of educational programmes; generating knowledge and developing technologies in scientific 'fields crucial to self-sustaining economic development; and creating a critical consciousness of the values and imperatives of national survival.

11.3. The deleterious consequences of non-investment or inadequate investment in education are indeed very serious. Similarly, the cost of neglecting vocational and technical education and of research is also unacceptable. Sub-optimal performance in these fields could cause irreparable damage to the Indian economy. The network of institutions set up from time to time since Independence to facilitate the application of science and technology would need to be substantially and expeditiously updated, since they are fast becoming obsolete.

11.4. In view of these Imperatives, education will be treated as a crucial area ot investment for nationl development and survival. The National Policy on Education, 1968, had laid down that the Investment on education be gradually increased to reach a level of expenditure of 6 percent of the national income as early as possible. Since the actual level of investment has remained far short of that target, it is important that greater determination be shown now to find the funds for the programmes laid-down in this Policy. While the actual requirements will be computed from time to time on the basis of monitoring and review, the outlay on education will be shaped up to the extent essential for policy implementation in the Seventh plan. It will be ensured that from the Eighth Five Year Plan onwards it will uniformly exceed to 6 percent of the National income.

Review

11.5. The implementation of the various parameters of the New Policy must be reviewed every five years. Appraisals at short, intervals will, also, be made to ascertain the progress of implementation and the trends emerging from time to time.

PART XII
THE FUTURE

12.1. The future shape of education in India is too complex to envision with precision. Yet, given our tradition which has almost always put a high premium on intellectual and spiritual attainment, we are bound to succeed in achieving our objectives.

12.2. The main task is to strengthen the base of the, pyramid, - which might come close to a billion people at the turn of the century. Equally, it is important to ensure that those at the top of the pyramid are among the best in the world. Our cultural well-springs had taken good care of both ends in the past; the skew set in with foreign domination and influence. It should now be possible to further intensify the nation-wide effort in "Human Resource Development," with Education playing its multi-faceted role.

Ministry of Human Resource Development, Government of India, Department of Education, New Delhi, May 1986

3.3 Agriculture and Biotechnology

Panditji had said – Everything can wait but not agriculture. That has not changed. Indiraji had desired agriculture as our **Adimantra.** It shows the kind of importance that has been given to agriculture in the past. Realising that agriculture was the backbone of the Indian economy, Rajiv Gandhi stressed upon the need for faster and even agricultural growth, which required the extension of green revolution to other regions, say, in the North-Eastern part of India. Rajiv Gandhi further stated that—

> *One of the biggest challenges that we are facing is that of drought and, in some areas, very severe floods. These underline the need to link the scientific efforts with the reality as it exists on the ground. It is important to do research at the frontiers, in blue – sky areas, and we must continue that. But it is equally important for us to concentrate on those areas which will affect the life, the livelihood of our people today and our indigenous scientific effort must look at the challenges that the country is facing now.*[1]

This was his concern over the crisis of agricultural development. He said -

> *Indian agriculture can be divided into two phases; the first half of the twentieth century, during which period it was for all practical purposes absolutely stagnant and stationary, no meaningful development took place at all; and Indian agriculture in the second half of this century where we have seen a stagnant, dormant agriculture blossom into one of the major Green Revolution areas of the world. We have seen during these past two years of drought that our agriculture has gained the resilience to face up to tremendous challenges. What has made this happen? What is the difference between the first half and the second half of the twentieth century?*
>
> *The difference is basically the scientific knowledge, scientific input and equally important, their application*

at the field level, which means it is the team work between our scientists, our extension workers and our farmers that had led to this. But the beginnings, the roots of this growth are very definitely in the science and technology that has been applied to the farm sector. With science and technology, in a very short period, we have transformed India, formerly a country of famines and shortages, into a country that is strong, resilient, self-sufficient. It is a success story for the whole world to see.

Agriculture is the most important part of our economy and of our developmental process. ...As we look towards the next century, when we think of how India is to develop, when we think of new technologies, new science for India, our attention must remain centered on the agricultural sector. This will be so for many years. We have to see how we can develop our agriculture, to break the hold of poverty, ...

When we talk of high technology today, we are talking about bio – engineering, we are talking of better power for agriculture, better implements, better tools. We are talking of better forecasts for the rains, the monsoons. All this requires a very high level of technology. When we talk of monsoons, we need the biggest computers to be able to predict rains and do research on the monsoons. So, if we start with the field and the farmer, and work backwards to see what is needed to support that farmer, we cover almost every section of our scientific and industrial development.

It is when these developments are coordinated that fine progress will take place. The breakthrough will come when the technology is brought together with proper extension work, so that the benefits can go from the lab right down to the farmer's field.[2]

Rajiv Gandhi said - it was his faith in science apart from other considerations, which made him feel: "We have achieved Green Revolution mostly in wheat in the North – Western parts of India. Today our wheat production has gone up almost sevenfold. Our food reserves are very large. A country which was dependent on wheat imports is not only self – sufficient, but has more than enough. We have to replicate this in other parts of the country and with other crops. The areas where we would like concentration are the semi-arid areas – the zones where productivity is very low, where poverty is still a very major problem. If our agricultural institutions can give a thrust that will break poverty in these areas, that will increase purchasing power which will then snow-ball and develop the entire region. ... the real challenge is to increase the productivity and lower the cost of production. ... This means hard work in the lab. But perhaps more important it means going out and passing on your knowledge to the farmers, not just in the areas where development has taken place (because that is much easier) but in those areas where development has been slower, where agricultural productivity has not increased"[3]. He further said -

> *Perhaps the one key factor for better agricultural productivity is land reforms. This is an area where a lot has been talked about, a lot of work has been done in some areas, but by and large, it has fallen by the wayside. We are committed to tackle this problem and see that land reforms do take place and take place effectively. We are now studying what has happened in the past and soon we will be coming out with a programme, which we will implement, hopefully fast.*[4]

A man of practical and positive nature, Rajiv Gandhi stated : "Our farmers have demonstrated that they are capable of using front-line technologies. That is why we are self-sufficient in food today. *And, if our farmers, who perhaps could have been considered one of the most backward groups as far as scientific education is concerned, are capable of this jump, then almost every section of our society is capable of absorbing technology. We have to see that we create the correct educational environment for them to be able to absorb these."*[5]

He further said that -

> *Scientists need to look at the way we use our water resources. India is one of the most favoured regions of the world in the amount of rainfall it receives. True, the rain is concentrated in a few months, but, we must learn why, inspite of this, we are now short of water, even in those areas which receive normal rainfall. Dry land farming and water management should be near the top of the scientists' agenda. ... Science and technology must tell us how to protect our soil fertility, how to create the correct balance and distribution of forest cover, and right kind of cropping patterns. It must warn us, when warning is needed, of the implications of pumping pernicious waste into the atmosphere and using chemicals to increase crop yields. These are but a few of the areas to tackle. If we do not take action, disaster will surely overtake us. Science must squarely face the challenges of sustainable growth.*[6]

Besides the announcement of National Seed Policy in 1986, he initiated bold steps to aid the farmers in attaining good growth, self-sufficiency in food, as well as, nutritional adequacy. These include restoration of credit facility from NABARD, short-term production credit, special credits for rain-fed farming and issuing of Passbooks and credit cards for the farmers. While making a statement on the new Agricultural Package for India, in Lok Sabha on 10 October 1989, Rajiv Gandhi said that –

> *"...the time has come to reiterate that the highest national priority must be given to the farmer, to farming, to food and agriculture as the cornerstone of our economy. ... Therefore, we are determined to accord the highest priority to agriculture in the Eighth Five Year Plan, 1990-95. Agricultural growth must be accelerated. Agricultural income and employment must grow faster than they have in the past.*[7]

In a country like India, the demands from the agricultural sector are increasing very rapidly. The demands increase with the increase of population, but the demands also increase because the quality of life has gone up and logically the demand on agriculture has also gone up. We have matched most of these demands with the peaks in our production, but we must remember that every peak in our production is only the base camp for the next summit that we must strive towards". Rajiv Gandhi made the above statement at the Silver Jubilee Convocation of the Indian Agricultural Research Institute (IARI), New Delhi on 6 February 1986. His remarks show a mind equipped to guide and oversee policy matters even in areas where he had no personal expertise. He further said –

> *Looking back at the Green Revolution, we must give much of the credit for this to the IARI. The IARI must now look towards how to achieve the same in other areas. Perhaps the first area to concentrate on should be rice – high yielding better qualities of rice with better productivity. Our productivity of rice is still very low – under two tones per hectare – while other countries have already gone over five. These are the sorts of challenges that you have to face. You have to see how better technologies can be brought in – technologies not just in the search for better seeds, but better methods in fertilizer use, better utilization of the resources. Are we using too much fertilizer? Can we do better? Are we using too much water? Can we economize and get better productivity from less water? These are the types of questions that you must address your minds to.*

With a view to attaining true progress, he stressed upon the need of coordinating and networking the progress of other sectors. He said at the IARI Convocation on 6 February 1986, that –

> *Agricultural science has opened up exciting new vistas for biotechnology, tissue culture, genetic engineering.*

Indian scientists have made a major contribution, at home and abroad, to the development of these technologies. We have invested $20 billion in irrigation to increase three-fold the irrigated area and taken electricity to hundreds of thousands of villages. We now have the potential to dramatically increase the output of irrigated crops like rice, fruits and vegetables as also dry land crops like coarse grain, pulses and oilseeds.

Our biggest problem today in the agricultural sector is oilseeds. A thrust-mission for oilseeds production was set up to deliver the finished product of vegetable oil to the consumer.

Self-Reliance and Innovation

We have consolidated and reinforced our unity, integrity and democracy through our processes of planning for development. Two basic principles have informed our system of planning: self-reliance and priority of the poor. We understand self-reliance to mean paying our own way, standing on our own feet. As Panditji put it: *"Nobody can bear our burdens for us; we have to bear them ourselves".* We hold ourselves responsible for our own development. We are not prepared to mortgage that responsibility to others. We are not prepared to put in jeopardy our hard-won independence nor restrict our freedom of action. We are not prepared to abnegate our responsibility to build, on the basis of the quintessential values of our civilization and the vision of our founding fathers, an India which stands as an example for the world. Therefore, nearly 93 per cent of the investment we have made in development over the last four decades has come from our own resources.

However, self-reliance, in our view, does not mean isolation from the international community or the global economy. That is why we have willingly sought – and given – economic and technical cooperation, we have, however, stressed that such cooperation can only be on terms compatible with our honour as a nation, our independence as a State and our self-reliance as an economy. We recognize the essential inter-dependence of the economies of the world. That is why we affirm the need for an international economic order based on cooperation and justice, not exploitation and dominance. Panditji described this as:

> *...enlightened self-interest, realizing that if some parts of the world do not progress, remain backward, they have an adverse effect on the whole economy of the world and they tend to drag down those parts that are at present prosperous.*

The other key element in our planning has been priority to the poor. That too has helped hold the country together and place us in a position to fulfill our larger global responsibilities. I recall Panditji's words in the Lok Sabha in a speech made early in our experience of planned development. He said:

> *We often go at a tangent on grounds of provincialism, communalism, religion or caste. We have no emotional awareness of the unity of the country. Planning will help us in having an emotional awareness of our problems as a whole. It will help us to see the isolated problems in villages or districts or even provinces in their largest text.*

> *The poor constitute the vast majority of our country. They constitute the majority of every ethnic, linguistic and religious group in the country. Poverty cuts across every category. In making the poor the focus of our planning, and in ensuring that the members of any one ethnic group are neither favoured nor discriminated against, we have pressed planning into the task of uniting the nation and given our people a common stake in political stability and economic progress.*

> *Poverty eradication is not merely a question of specific programmes. It is, above all, a political mindset. In his*

Panditji, in a rather more down to earth way, made the poor the focus of all planned development. He made us understand that, whatever the specific task at hand, the emphasis on eradicating poverty in the shortest time possible has to permeate one's consciousness. Let me illustrate this proposition with regard to industrialization and technology as they affect poverty removal.

Self-reliance, according to Indira Gandhi is not an "inward looking isolationist approach but a policy which ensures that decision making and key aspects of the pattern and content of development will remain firmly in national hands. A country of our size and potential cannot but aim at self-reliance. It is the ability of the scientists and technologists in the long-run, to develop India's capability to absorb and improve technology that is relevant to her economic growth. Industry should actively participate in the research, design and development programmes with the national R & D laboratories. Indian Industry should attain self-reliance in many sectors of the economy.

References

1. Rajiv Gandhi — Foundation Day celebrations, CSIR, 26 September 1987.
2. — Foundation stone Laying ceremony, Lal Bahadur Shastri Centre for Advanced Centre for Biotechnology and Plant Protection, 4 October 1988.
3. — Silver Jubilee Celebrations, IARI, New Delhi, 6 February 1986.
4. — 73rd Session, Indian Science Congress Association, New Delhi, 8 January 1986.
5. — 75th Session, Indian Science Congress Association, Pune, 7 January 1988.
6. — Statement on New Agiricultural Package, Lok Sabha, 10 October 1989.
7. — Nehru Centenary Memorial Lecture, New Delhi, 13 November 1989.

Government of India
Ministry of Agriculture, Department of Agriculture and Cooperation

No. 11-71/88-SD.1
New Delhi, September 16, 1988

Subject:- **NEW POLICY ON SEED DEVELOPMENT**

Encouraging seed production on commercial lines

1.1 Seed is a vital input for agricultural production. At present, seed multiplication programmes, particularly for cereals, are largely being implemented with governmental initiative through the National Seeds Corporation of India, State Farms Corporation of India and the State Seeds Corporations. A vast magnitude of quality seeds of different crops is required to meet the needs of the farmers. It is necessary to supplement governmental efforts by encouraging seed production on commercial lines so that a spirit of competition is promoted and employment potential generated.

Advantage of agro climatic zones

1.2 The variety of agro-climatic zones in the country confers the advantage of not only growing crops throughout the year but also producing seeds of crops, which thrive in temperate, sub-tropical and tropical latitudes and at different levels of humidity and soil moisture.

Upgradation of planting materials

1.3 The continuous upgradation of seeds/ planting materials of various crops is essential to maximise productivity per unit area. Besides fulfilling the internal requirements, seed industry can also be developed to cater to the requirements of foreign countries. Reputed foreign seed firms are already collaborating with private sector companies for the development of high yielding seeds in the country. Yet, the import, from time to time, of the best potential seed / planting materials available abroad, suitable for Indian agro-climatic conditions is necessary.

Provide the best planting materials to the farmers

1.4 Therefore policy initiatives should aim at providing to the Indian farmer the best planting materials available in the world to increase productivity, farm incomes and export earnings. Simultaneously, while importing seed planting material care has to be taken to ensure that there is absolutely no compromise on the requirements of plant quarantine procedures to prevent entry into the country of exotic pests, diseases and weeds, detrimental to Indian agriculture.

New Policy on Seed Development

2. After careful consideration of all the related aspects, a **New Policy on Seed Development** has been evolved with special emphasis on:-

[a] the import of high quality seeds;
[b] a time bound programme to strengthen modernise plant quarantine facilities:
[c] effective observance of procedures for quarantine/post entry quarantine [PEQ]; and
[d] incentives to encourage the domestic seed industry.

The existing Import Policy on Seeds

3.1 At present the import of living plants seeds or other plant materials is governed by the Special Licensing Procedures [para 104] and by the Import Policy for Registered Exporters of the Export & Import Policy (April, 1988 - March. 1991).

Plants Fruits & Seeds Order, 1984

3.2 All imports of seeds, plant materials etc. are regulated under the Plants, Fruits and Seeds [Regulation of Import into India] Order, 1984.

4. New Policy on Import of Seeds/Planting Materials

4.1 The New Policy for the import of Seeds and Planting Materials will cover the following categories:-

(i) Seeds of wheat and paddy;
(ii) Seeds of coarse cereals, oilseeds and pulses;
(iii) Seeds of vegetables, flowers and ornamental plants;
(iv) Tubers and bulbs of flowers;
(v) Cuttings/saplings etc. of flowers;
(vi) Seeds/planting materials of fruits.

Seeds of Wheat & Paddy

4.2 The ICAR has effective research collaboration with IRRI, Manila and CIMMYT, Mexico. In addition, germplasm of wheat and paddy is also being imported from various countries through the help of International Board of Plant Genetic Resources. Consequently no immediate imports of wheat and paddy seeds are considered necessary. However the Departments of Agriculture and Cooperation (DAC) and Agricultural Research and Education (DARE) will keep in close touch with the FAO / CGIAR in regard to the latest developments abroad in wheat and paddy.

Seeds of Coarse Cereals, Oilseeds and Pulses

4.3.1 It is necessary to increase the production of coarse cereals, oilseeds and pulses by making available high yielding seeds to the farmers. At the same time, repetitive bulk imports of these seeds cannot be permitted indefinitely. Based' on these considerations, the new import policy for seeds for sowing of coarse cereals, oilseeds and pulses is detailed in the following paragraphs.

Agreement to supply parent

4.3.2 The import of seeds of coarse cereals, pulses and oilseeds for sowing may be allowed

line seeds/ breeder seeds/ technology

for a period, not exceeding two years by companies, which have technical/financial collaboration agreements for production of seed with companies abroad, provided the foreign supplier agrees to supply parent line seeds/ nucleus or breeder seeds/technology to the Indian company within a period of two years from the date of import of the first commercial consignment after its import has been recommended by DAC.

NSC, SSC's may import

4.3.3 The National Seeds Corporation and the State Seeds Corporations may be permitted to import seeds of coarse cereals, oil seeds and pulses on the recommendations of DAC without being subject to the conditions stipulated in para 4.3.2.

Issue of Import license by the CCI&E

4.3.4 The import licence will be granted by the CCIE only on the recommendations of the DAC and subject to the provisions of the Plants, Fruits, and Seeds [Regulation of Import into India] Order, 1984.

Seed for trial evaluation by ICAR

4.3.5 A quantity of 5 kg of seed of coarse cereals /pulses and oilseeds for sowing, sought to be imported by eligible importers, will be given to ICAR or such farms, which are accredited by ICAR, for trial and evaluation. After trial/evaluation for one crop season, the ICAR, will intimate the results, agro-climatic zone-wise. Within three months of the season to DAC. After the receipt of the results of the ICAR trial/evaluation, an eligible importer may apply for the import of such seed to the DAC.

Recommendation of DAC

4.3.6 On receipt of the application for commercial import, the DAC will consider the trial/ evaluation report on the performance /resistance to seed and soil borne diseases of the seeds proposed to be imported. DAC may within 30 days of the receipt of the application, reject the application or recommend it to the CCI&E for grant of an import licence to the importer. The CCI&E shall issue the import licence within 15 days of the receipt of the recommendations from DAC.

Publicity through Media

4.3.7 The characteristics of the varieties/hybrids cleared by DAC for import shall be given publicity through the AIR, Doordarshan and the extension agencies so that farmers will get to know the potential of the varieties/hybrids cleared for import, as compared to the indigenous varieties/hybrids. The decision to import or not to import the varieties/ hybrids cleared by DAC will be left to the importers during the stipulated two year period.

Samples to ICAR/Gene Bank

4.3.8 All importers shall make available a small but specified quantity of the seed being imported to the ICAR at cost price, for testing / accession to the Gene Bank with the NBPGR.

Quaratine

4.3.9 The bulk import of seeds of coarse cereals, oil seeds and pulses shall be cleared / rejected by the PPA after quarantine checks within a period not exceeding three weeks. The rejected consignment shall be destroyed in accordance with the prescribed procedure.

Storage in bonded ware-house pending quarantine

4.3.10 During quarantine the imported consignment shall be kept in a customs bonded warehouse at the cost of the importer.

Vegetables and flowers

4.4.1 The availability of high yielding vegetable seeds is essential for increasing vegetable production and productivity. The additional production will generate higher incomes to the farmers and ensure the increased availability of vegetables at reasonable prices to the consumers.

4.4.2 Further, there is a significant demand for fresh vegetables and flowers in the international market. The production, on a competitive basis, of vegetables and flowers of international standards has to be developed/accelerated to increase our export earnings.

Import on OGL

4.4.3 It is, therefore, necessary to supply to the farmers the best available seeds of vegetables / flowers and ornamental plants. Accordingly, the import of seeds of vegetables/flowers and ornamental plants, tubers and bulbs, cuttings, saplings, budwoods, etc. of flowers will be allowed on OGL by identified categories.

Categories eligible to import

4.4.4 The following categories shall be eligible to import these seeds/planting materials:

(i) Departments of Agriculture / Horticulture of the State Governments. State Agriculture Universities and ICAR;
(ii) Seed producing Indian companies / firms) after registration 'with the National Seeds Corporation:
(iii) National Seeds Corporation. State Seeds Corporations;
(iv) Food processing industrial units;
(v) Growers of vegetables and flowers registered with the Director of Agriculture / Horticulture of the State Government.

No PEQ for seeds of vegetables/ flowers and tubers & bulbs

4.4.5 No post entry quarantine (PEQ) shall be necessary for the import of seeds of vegetables / flowers / ornamental plants and tubers and bulbs of flowers. The import will be permitted after visual inspection, fumigation laboratory inspection and grow-out tests.

4.4.6 The Plant Protection Adviser to the

Government of India [PPA] may reject / clear the consignment of seeds of vegetables / flowers / ornamental plants and tubers and bulbs of flowers within a period not exceeding 50 days. The consignment shall be kept in a bonded warehouse at the cost of the importer until quarantine / customs clearance is given. The customs clearance of seeds of vegetables / flowers / ornamental plants and tubers and bulbs of flowers will be given by the customs authorities only after the quarantine clearance is given by the PPA.

PEQ required for cuttings and saplings etc. of flowers

4.4.7 For import of cuttings, saplings, budwood etc. of flowers, PEQ shall be essential. PEQ facilties as may be prescribed by the PPA, shall have to be established by the eligible categories of importers permitted to import cuttings, saplings. bud wood etc., of flowers under OGL. The fact that such a facility has been established has to be certified by either the PPA or an agency authorised by him under the Plants, Fruits & Seeds [Regulation of Import into India] Order, 1984. This agency, hereinafter referred to as the designated inspection agency [DIA], which may be the State Agriculture University [SAU], will also be authorised to carry out the PEQ inspection. The DIA's certificate that the importer has established the prescribed PEQ facility shall be presented by the eligible importer to the PPA before the imported consignment is given quarantine clearance by the PPA.

4.4.8 The quarantine clearance subject to the PEQ condition will be given by the PPA after conducting visual inspection / laboratory inspection to see that the consignment of the imported cuttings, saplings, budwood etc. of flowers, is free from any exotic pests or diseases.

Custom clearance for vegetable/ flowers and ornamental plants, tubers bulbs of flowers	4.4.9 Customs clearance shall be given by the customs authorities to the consignment on receipt of the quarantine clearance with PEQ condition from PPA.
Approval of PEQ facility	4.4.10 Cuttings, saplings, budwoods etc. of flowers which require PEQ inspection shall be grown in the PEQ facility, approved by the PPA or a DIA authorised by the PPA. The period for which the cuttings, saplings, budwoods etc. shall be grown in such a facility shall be specified in the import permit to be granted by the PPA.
Guidelines to designated inspection agency for PEQ	4.4.11 Detailed guidelines for the DIA [Appendix 'A') for conducting post entry quarantine shall be laid down by the PPA from time to time. Should the PEQ reveal any exotic pest or disease the material shall be forthwith destroyed in the prescribed manner by the DIA under intimation to PPA.
Samples to ICAR/ Gene Bank	4.4.12 Small quantities of flower / vegetable seeds, tubers / bulbs and cuttings and saplings will be made available by the importers to ICAR at cost price for testing / accession to the Gene Bank.
Modification in REP Policy	4.5 The import of seeds of vegetables, flowers, ornamental plants and bulbs and tubers of flowers, will continue to be allowed under REP. However, the transfer of REP licences for items of seeds of vegetables / flowers / ornamental plants, bulbs and tubers of flowers will be allowed only to those

persons who are otherwise eligible to import these items under OGL subject to the conditions laid down in the Plants, Fruits & Seeds [Regulation of Import into India] Order, 1984.

Import Policy for seeds/ Planting Materials for fruits

4.6 The import of seeds / planting material for fruits shall be permitted selectively by DAC, on a case-to-case basis on the recommendation of the State Director of Horticulture/Agriculture, subject to such quarantine regulations as may be laid down by the PPA.

5. Strengthening of Quarantine Facilities and Plant Quarantine Procedures

Introduction of pests and pathogens

5.1 In the past, several pests and pathogens have been introduced through seed material imported into the country. Many of these pests have since become wide-spread. Some examples are downy mildew on sunflower, spotted wilt virus on tomato. peanut stripe virus on groundnut apple scab from Europe, golden nematode and wart diseases of potato from Europe and bacterial blight of paddy from East Asia to mention only a few.

No compromise on quarantine facilities

5.2 Therefore, while importing seeds and planting materials it has to be ensured that there is absolutely no compromise on plant quarantine procedures. Every effort has to be made to prevent the entry into India of exotic pests diseases and weeds, which are detrimental to the interests of the farmers. The new policy on imports for seeds can thus be implemented fully only after the plant quarantine facilities are adequately strengthened within a specified time frame.

Imports allowed from Delhi,

5.3 There are 26 quarantine and fumigation stations located at 10 airports 9 seaports and 7 land frontiers. It is proposed to allow import of seed

Bombay, Calcutta, Madras and Amritsar

/ planting material etc. initially only at Delhi, Bombay, Calcutta, Madras and Amritsar. Therefore. the plant quarantine facilities at these five centres are being strengthened/modernised.

Strengthening of plant quarantine facilities

5.4 The strengthening of the Plant Quarantine organisation through the augmentation of technical staff provision of physical infrastructure, essential laboratory equipment and the creation of regional offices for issue of import permits shall be a time-bound operation and shall be completed within a period of 12 months.

The New Policy effective from 1st Oct, 88

5.5 The new policy on import of seed shall come into effect from the 1st October 1988.

Imports subject to availability of quarantine facilities

5.6 The imports under the new policy shall be allowed, based on the procedures being followed by PPA and subject to the existing physical facilities of the Plant Quarantine & Fumigation Stations to undertake laboratory tests, fumigation etc. for a period of three months i.e. till the 31st December, 1988.

Phased implementation

5.7 During this 3 month period, PPA, while strengthening the quarantine facilities will also firm up arrangements for utilising the facilities for grow-out tests available at the IARI New Delhi and the SAUs or other research laboratories near Bombay, Calcutta, Madras and Amritsar. By the 1st of October, 1989, based on the time-bound programme, the plant quarantine facilities at the 5 stations should have been augmented to implement the new policy in full. Pending this from the 1st January to the 1st October 1989. the implementation of the new policy will be phased / regulated, based on the progress in the commissioning of the new plant quarantine facilities at these five stations.

National Plant Quarantine Advisory Committee

5.8 A National Plant Quarantine Advisory Committee shall be constituted to advise the PPA on various technical matters in different disciplines of Entomology, Plant Pathology, Nematology, Virology, Bacteriology, Weed Sciences and for serological detection techniques of viruses. This Committee may meet at least twice a year.

6. Guiudelines and Procedures for quarantine / Post Entry Quarantine

Plant Quarantine Counters

6.1 A separate Plant Quarantine Counter shall be provided in the arrival hall at Delhi, Bombay, Calcutta, Madras and Amritsar airports and at Bombay, Calcutta and Madras sea ports for effectively checking the imported seeds and planting materials and ensuring strict observance of plant quarantine procedures.

Pre-entry requirements

6.2 All consignments of seeds and plants for sowing shall be imported into India in accordance with the provisions of Plants, Fruits, and Seeds (Regulation of Import into India) Order, 1984. An import permit and a phytosanitary certificate with additional declaration if necessary as prescribed by the PPA, shall be essential. The pre-entry requirements for flowers and ornamental plants, vegetable seeds (FVS), bulbs and tubers (ST) and cuttings and saplings (CS) would be as follows:

	Requirement	*FVS*	*BT*	*CS*
[i]	Import permit (E)	R	R	R
[ii]	Phytosanitary Certificate (PSC:E)	R	R	R
[iii]	*Additional Declaration*			
[a]	Freedom from Soil (E)	R	R	R
[b]	Freedom from weeds	R	NR	NR
[c]	Plant Quarantine objects	R	R	R

iv] Approval of PEQ facilities NR NR R

[E =existing; R - required: NR - not required]

Entry Safeguard

6.3 After the arrival of consignments at the port of entry, quarantine checks would be undertaken which may include visual inspection, laboratory inspection, fumigation and grow out tests. For the purpose of these checks samples will be drawn and the tests will be conducted concurrently.

Post Entry Quarantine

6.4 PEQ will be required only for growing imported cuttings, saplings, budwood etc. of flowers. The importers will be required to create PEQ facilities, as may be prescribed by the PPA. The guidelines for PEQ facilities for importers are at Appendix 'B'. The planting materials, which require PEQ inspection, shall be grown in the PEQ facility approved by the PPA or the DIA in the State, authorised by the PPA under the provisions of the Plants, Fruits and Seeds [Regulation of Import into India] Order 1984. The period, for which the planting materials shall be grown in such a facility, shall be specified in the import permits granted by PPA. On the production of the certificate from the DIA that the importer has established the prescribed PEQ facility, the PPA will give the quarantine clearance after visual tests laboratory tests etc.

Sampling Procedures

6.5 The sampling procedures for various categories of imported vegetable / flower planting materials would be as under:-

(a) FVS The sampling techniques shall be as per International Seed Testing Association (ISTA) rules and guidelines.

The minimum sample size is considered to

be 10 numbers. However, in case of bulk imports. the representative sample for V.I. and L.I. would not be less than 0.1 %.

Inspection requirements

6.6 The inspection under the categories mentioned above would comprise the following specific investigations / parameters:

	Inspection	*FVS*	*BT*	*CS*
[i]	Sampling	As per ISTA Rules	Min. 10 numbers or 0.1%	
[ii]	V.I.	R	R	R
[iii]	L.I.			
	a] X-Radiography	R	NR	NR
	b] Washing Test	R	R	R
	c] Nematodes detection	R	R	R
	d] Incubation for diseases/pests	R	R	R
[iv]	G.T.	R	R	NR
[v]	PEQ	NR	NR	R by DIA
[v]	Total Duration [days]	45	50	Min.25 Max.45

[R = required NR = not required]

Grow out test, fumigation etc.

6.7 The technique for undertaking grow out tests has been prescribed by the PPA. The seeds of vegetables / flowers / ornamental plants after visual inspection shall be subject to fumigation at the cost of the importer to check pest infestation / disease before undertaking laboratory inspection.

Presence of exotic pests, diseases and nematodes

6.8 If the imported consignment shows the presence or manifestation of any exotic disease, pests or nematodes, the entire consignment shall be rejected and disposed of in accordance with the prescribed methods of destruction.

Pests, diseases nematodes recorded in India

6.9 The imported consignment showing presence of pests diseases and nematodes recorded in India shall be released only after effective quarantine measures are undertaken to bring down the incidence to levels prescribed; otherwise, such consignments shall be disposed of as prescribed by the PPA.

Release of consignments

6.10 If the samples drawn from the imported consignments satisfy the prescribed checks, the consignments shall be released for entry.

7. Incentives to Domestic Seed Industry

7.1 In the context of the liberalisation of the import of seed / planting materials, incentives are proposed to be provided to domestic seed industry to encourage and promote its growth and enable it to produce viable high yielding varieties / hybrids seeds at a faster pace to meet the internal requirements as well as to cater to export markets.

Reduction of Import Duty

7.2 Accordingly, it has been decided to reduce the import duty on seeds to 15%. The import duty reduction concession shall be accorded only to seeds meant for sowing and to planting materials.

Reduction of Import Duty on seed production/ processing quality control machinery and equipment

7.3 It is proposed to reduce the import duty on machines and equipments used for seed production / processing quality control machinery etc., not manufactured in the country or for which the technology upgradation is necessary. A list of such machines / equipments, which is being drawn up by the Department of Revenue in consultation with the DGTO and DAC, will be notified by the Department of Revenue.

Pre-shipment

7.4 Pre-shipment credit upto 180 days will be allowed at 9.5% rate of interest per annum.

credit — Beyond 180 duys. and in all uptc 270 days with the prior approval of the Reserve Bank of India, the rate of interest shall be 11.5% per annum. Post-shipment credit shall also be allowed at 9.5% rate of interest per annum. A circular specifically allowing these facilities to seed exporting units will be issued by the Reserve Bank of India.

Cash Compensatory Support — 7.5 Cash compensatory support on the export of seed will be considered by the Ministry of Commerce on the basis of data supplied by the seed exporting companies.

Income-Tax Rebate — 7.6 Income tax rebate / deduction will be given to the seed industry on the revenue expenditure incurred on in-house research and development, to such units which pay income tax.

Backward area subsidy for seed industry — 7.7 Incentives, as provided to industries located in the backward areas / growth centres, may be sought by DAC for seed industry. Such concessions for seed industry will be identified by DAC and taken up with the Ministry of Finance.

Monitoring by High Level Review Committee — 8. A High Level Review Committee in the DAC will monitor the progress of the implementation of the Policy.

New Policy to Benefit Seed Industry/ Farmers — 9. The New Policy on Seed Development should help the seed industry to grow. The farmers will be benefited by getting access to the available seed and planting material available anywhere in the world.

Cooperation of State — 10. The Government of India trusts that the State Governn Administrations of Union Territories

Governments / State Agricultural University will extend their fullest cooperation and assistance in implementation of the Policy.

APPENDIX - A

GUIDELINES FOR DESIGNATED INSPECTION AGENCIES UNDER THE PLANTS, FRUITS AND SEEDS (REGULATION OF IMPORT INTO INDIA) ORDER, 1984

1. Post entry quarantine (PEQ) shall be essential for imported cuttings, saplings, budwoods, etc. of flowers.

2. Eligible categories of importers permitted to import cuttings, saplings, budwoods, etc. of flowers must establish post entry quarantine facilities, as may be prescribed by the PPA.

3. A certificate shall be issued by the PPA or the Designated Inspection Agencies in the States authorised by the PP A under the Plants, Fruits and Seeds (Regulation of Import into India) Order, 1984 for conducting PEQ inspections, that the importer has established the prescribed PEQ facilities, after verification and evaluation of the PEQ facilities created by the importer.

4. Imported, cuttings, saplings, budwoods etc. of flowers shall be grown in the prescribed PEQ facility for a period specified in the import permit granted by the PPA.

5. The DIA shall be located in the State Agricultural University.

6. A multidisciplinary team of the DIA consisting of a Plant Pathologist / Virologist / Entymologist shall inspect the imported planting material at the time of planting in the specified PEQ facility.

7. Post planting observations shall be taken in the following manner:

   Cuttings The first observation would depend upon the growth of the plant but normally it should be undertaken within 20-25 days followed by second observation within 40-45 days of planting.

Saplings The first observation after planting shall depend upon the growth of the plant, which may normally be within 2-3 weeks.

During inspection, special notice should be taken of symptoms of any plant diseases, especially systemic and viral disease.

Disease affected plants should be destroyed in the presence of the DIA, as prescribed by PPA, to avoid any possible contamination by pathogens of the surrounding environment and plants.

In the event of observance of any exotic pest or disease, the material shall be forthwith destroyed in the prescribed manner under intimation to PPA.

8. The final report of PEQ inspection shall be sent to PPA for information and record within 15 days of the final observation.

APPENDIX- B

GUIDELINES FOR IMPORTERS FOR ESTABLISHING PEQ FACILITIES

1. The importers of cutting and saplings etc. of flowers will be required to establish post entry quarantine facilities, as prescribed by the Plant Protection Adviser. These facilities may include the establishment of a glass house / plastic house / any other specified facility, in a defined area, in isolation.

2. Imported cuttings, saplings, budwoods etc. of flowers shall be grown in the prescribed PEQ facility for a period specified in the import permit granted by the PPA.

3. The importer shall facilitate the Designated Inspection Agency (DIA) to undertake inspection at specified intervals of time.

4. The importer shall inform the DIA about the planting dates well in advance. If there is any occurrence of pest or disease symptoms, he shall immediately inform the DIA. The importer shall abide by the decision of the DIA.

5. No plant or parts thereof whether living or dead shall be removed during the pendency of post entry quarantine without the approval of the DIA.

6. A qualified Plant Pathologist / Entomologist / Plant Virologist / Horticulturist should be engaged as consultant at the cost of the importer for looking after the plants under post entry quarantine.

7. On the detection of any exotic pest or disease, the entire imported material shall be destroyed forthwith in a prescribed manner under intimation to PPA.

8. During inspection, the multidisciplinary team of the DIA shall take special notice of symptoms of any plant diseases specially systemic and viral diseases. The disease affected plants shall be destroyed in the presence of DIA to avoid possible contamination of the surrounding plants and environment by pathogens and the soil shall be disinfected with formaline.

9. The importer shall pay the cost of post entry quarantine inspection, as prescribed by PP A. He shall make the deposit, as may be laid down, on the quarantine clearance of the consignment by the PP A. The consignment shall be released only after the importer makes the payment in full of the DIA inspection fees to the PPA.

10. The importer shall maintain basic inspection tools like hand lenses, microscopes, chemicals, dissection box, glass vials and petri plates.

11. A log book shall be maintained for proper record for incoming and outgoing material as well as the dates of inspection and detailed report by the DIA.

12. A register containing details of imported material, planting date, manifestation of diseases and appearance of pests and control measures taken shall be maintained.

13. The PEQ areas shall have the provision of locking arrangements for security purposes.

3.4 TECHNOLOGY MISSIONS

Technology by itself is not enough; sociology is to be part of it. As a major initiative, Rajiv Gandhi launched the concept of Technology Missions. The concept of these missions and the way they were implemented, deserve to be emphasized, as a major technology management breakthrough. The mission-oriented approach was a model on how to create an organizational structure for the purpose, spelling-out clear-cut goals, schedules and organizing finance for the whole exercise. The concerned ministries and the Government departments were assigned the task of coordinating with all Science and Technology departments for providing inputs towards the successful implementation of the projects. For instance, in solving the water problem, he was not satisfied by only targeting the source, but would delve into the intricacies of conveying the supply to the threshold. He said -

> *We have come out with the idea of having Missions. ... Now, my concept of Missions was a limited number of fields with very specific targets. ... The idea and concept of a Mission was that we choose, say half a dozen or maximum of ten areas where we can really do well. Ten areas where in five years or ten years, we will be the leaders in technology or in science in those particular areas. We try to target those areas in directions that will give us a direct fall out.*
>
> *... But they must be Missions, which go all the way from A to Z. This will involve more than just the scientific community. The science part could develop it. The technology part we would try to implement it and fit it into real life on the ground. ...*
>
> *The concept is that we would give much more freedom, remove all the strings in these areas, and give proper funding to see that we can make real progress as we did in space, as we did in atomic energy, as we did in a number of areas. But wherever we have made this progress, it appears to be because a specific target had been given, a group of people had been chosen*

> *and told O.K., now you go ahead and do it, without too much interference in what they are doing on a day-to-day basis. The idea of Missions is to do this.*[1]

He said - Science and technology have to be the key for our development. Our thrust is for our people, on anti-poverty programmes and for socially relevant areas. We are setting up a number of scientific missions and thrust areas to see that funding, proper scientific management and all the resources that are refined in these areas are available. One of the areas that we have chosen is drinking water. This may sound simple. But it involves the highest level of scientific and technological input. Other areas are oilseeds development, immunization of children, and education of illiterates.[2]

He further said - "We have decided on a number of Missions. Already five had been established. Drinking water – it might sound simple that will just be digging holes in the ground and pulling out water, but out of all these five Missions, the maximum amount of scientific development and technological development will go into drinking water and the highest technology, out of any of these Missions, will be used to give drinking water specially in these areas where there is a tremendous shortage of drinking water.

Another Mission will be that of oil seeds and another vaccination for children – vaccination for the health of our children and eradication of illiteracy. "... Oil Seed Mission, for example means development of the oil seeds in a genetic laboratory, transferring that into the extension work of actually getting it to the farmer, explaining to the farmer, how he is going to use it, turning his produce into oil, marketing the oil and getting it to the consumer, and keeping the cost right across the exercise.... So these are extremely complicated exercises, which will cut across many ministries, many state governments, and if these are to succeed, we would really need good men at the top, who would be able to really cut through all this red tape and deliver the results that are required if this country has to survive."[3]

For the first time, the concept of a Mission Approach was conceived and initiated during the Seventh Five – Year Plan period

(1984-89). It was recognized that this approach (say from A to Z) would first define the total task to be accomplished and all the components needed for this purpose including the S & T components. The latter will be accomplished by scientists who may expect to see the fruition of their work in achieving end – results through establishment of live organic linkages between various organizational structures, including administrative ministries, financial aspects, coordination between various scientific components and institutions concerned with these, and actual field work. A mission oriented ethos, it was felt, would introduce a sense of urgency with clear-cut time and cost schedules, monitoring mechanisms and a new management approach.

Six National Technology Missions in areas of direct relevance to the society and envisaging entirely new management approaches were launched. These covered: oilseeds, mass immunization, better communications, drinking water supply, reduction of illiteracy, and milk production. These missions were assigned to a concerned nodal Ministry, which coordinated with all the concerned science and other departments who were responsible for inputs for successful implementation of the task.

Similarly, nine science and technology projects in the Mission Mode were taken up during the 7th Plan. The emphasis was on an end-to-end approach with significant research and development but connected with financial, administrative and management aspects. The emphasis was to demonstrate that, over a period of time, scientific ideas and research and development efforts can be translated through feasibility field trials/pilot plant work to an operationalisation phase/widespread production and use. The overall tasks involved multi-institutional and multi-agency endeavour. These projects were:

1. Immunological Approaches to Fertility control
2. Integrated Vector Control of Malaria and other vector-borne Diseases.
3. National Goitre Control Programme: Full coverage of UP, within 7th Five-year plan: S & T Inputs for Monitoring.
4. Development and Production of Immuno-diagnostics.

5. Cattle Herd Improvement for Increased Productivity using Embryo Transfer Technology.
6. Operationalisation of National Natural Resources Management Systems (NNRMS) and Natural Resources Data Management Systems (NRDMS).
7. National Centre for Medium Range Weather Forecasting (setting up of) and Development of Agro-meteorological services.
8. Development of Amorphous Silicon Solar Cell Technology.

Rajiv Gandhi said *...We have set up a number of Technology Missions, which start with the frontiers of science and hopefully will end up in the homes of our people, in their daily lives. If India is to win this struggle against poverty, it is only with the most modern and best methods that we stand a chance, we look forward to you and many other scientists like you to help us in this giant step that the Country has to take*[4].

He further said -

The application of science at the grass roots, although of fundamental importance to the development efforts, has not received quite the same attention. It is an imbalance that seriously needed rectification, we are now attempting to rectify this through Technology Missions ...What we need to establish are adequate linkages between science and technology, on the one hand, and the economic and productive sectors, on the other. ...The Technology Missions are directly related to our highest national priority, the war on poverty.[5]

To a question, that why was it that we could launch satellites and make rockets, but we could not give drinking water, Rajiv Gandhi replied that *it was not a lack of technology, it was a lack of being able of to apply that technology, at the right point.* The system was not working and that is where the Technology Mission comes in .He explained that the drinking water Mission marries that remote sensing of aquifires with the plumber, the mason, and the electrician who are required to install, operate and maintain a hand pump.[6] Rajiv Gandhi was the Prime mover of the vitally important Technology Mission in India. He remarked at the National Conference on Telecommunications on 3 February 1987, that –

> *In our country, the numbers of PCOs are much too few. We need to really look at our indigenous problems and having analysed them, go for solutions to our own problems instead of trying to match our problems to ready-made solutions. It cannot work that way. This is one of the reasons that we have paid so much attention to telecom in the past few years. We have tried to have a holistic approach to the whole problem for quicker access, for faster communication – an approach that will link the urban centers, urban and rural areas and also provide linkages between the rural areas. We must coordinate all the activities that we are doing in the telecom sector, and to do this, we thought the best method is to have a Technology Mission; one umbrella which would look right from the R & D problem, right from the laboratory to the home of the user and try to overcome all the hurdles that we face in that area.*

References

1. Rajiv Gandhi —Conference on Science and Technology in India: Retrospect and Prospect, New Delhi, 13 November 1985.
2. — Speech, during the debate on the President's address, Lok Sabha, 27 February 1986.
3. — Speech in the Lok Sabha, 10 April 1986.
4. — Conf. of the Directors of National Laboratories, CSIR, New Delhi, 28 May 1986.
5. —76th Session, Indian Science Congress Association, Madurai, 3 January 1989.
6. Sonia Gandhi – *Rajiv,* Viking Penguin Books, New Delhi, pg. 124, 1992.

3.5 Inculcation of Scientific Temper

Tomorrow's India will have to be very different from today's India just as today's India's is very different from India of 1948-50, Who could have dreamed 38 years ago that India would be launching its own satellite and that India would be at the forefront of nuclear development? It was unimaginable. But here we are today, not just in these two fields, but there are other fields like defence, electronics, where we are as good as anybody else, because Panditji had the vision to sow the seed- said Rajiv Gandhi at the Nehru Science Centre, Mumbai on 11 November, 1985.

> *Panditji set the mood for developing a scientific temper in the country. It was not an easy task at that time with a newly independent, very poor country to strike out in such a direction. But Panditji had the vision to realise that it was only with science and technology that India could lift itself up and today we are where we are because Panditji and Indiraji put that thrust in science and technology.*
>
> *... Ultimately, what will help us to develop a real base for science and technology is an involvement of the average person with science and technology. Whether it is a question of appliances that he is using at home, whether it is in the fields where a farmer is using technology, unless, this scientific temper, as Panditji said, really seeps down to our society, we will never be able to get the inputs for science that are within our capability, which are available to us, but are just not being allowed to develop.*[1]

One of the key factors has to be that of developing a scientific temper like Panditji had said so often. Without that scientific temper, it cannot be possible and a scientific temper must come into the average Indian, if he is to start developing? It can be brought about by media, it can be brought about by education and we must do everything that we can to bring this about. We are looking at this from the starting point and that is the New Education Policy.[2] He further said -

Last year, in 1988, we have brought out a New Education Policy, which we feel will bring down many of these barriers. It will need the cooperation of the scientific community. It will need fresh guidelines, which must come in now in the initial implementation stages, to see that right temper is developed. It will require much greater involvement of the scientific community in the education system. We cannot afford that community to be isolated and un-involved and then expect a scientific temper and lot of bright minds developing in the country.[3]

Indian science has come has a long way since Independence. It owes much to the vision of one man, Jawaharlal Nehru. ... He described his relationship with science in the following words: *"I too have worshipped at the shrine of science and counted myself as one of its votaries"*. He placed the highest importance on the cultivation of a scientific temper. He saw science and technology as the motor of modernization. Thus he saw science as holding the key to developing both a better human being and a better society. Indiraji continued the policy adding new dimensions to the thrust of our scientific temper.[4] The development of a scientific temper was one of the key factors for progress among the average Indian and not among the scientists alone, believed Rajiv Gandhi. He said –

Once we have a scientific temper, basically it will remove the fear of the unknown, which keeps people back, which keeps people from moving ahead and using the tools that are available to them. The scientific temper will help develop an inquisitive spirit ... It is only when we start thinking ... that a scientific temper will develop and we ourselves will start improving the tools that we have got and that we live with.[5]

We have not gone from a scientific temper to industrialization, but we have industrialization leading to a scientific temper. Therefore, there is too much a race, which leads to imitation, and too little innovation. We need to break out of this rut. We need bold, revolutionary, assertive and aggressive thinking. We must reject what is inadequate; we must try to secure the best – said Rajiv Gandhi at Science Congress Bangalore, on 3 January 1987.[6]

Scientific Awareness

> *Development and science are related. Underdevelopment by definition is the lack of being able to use modern science and technology for the benefit of our people to increase their productivity; to increase their comforts, to improve their life span. If we are going to break this barrier, it must come from scientific institutions and our scientists, technologists and industrialists* – said Rajiv Gandhi, while addressing the Conference of Directors of National laboratories of the Council of Scientific and Industrial Research, New Delhi on 28 May 1986.

While inaugurating the Conference on "Science and Technology in India, Retrospect and Prospect" on 13 November 1985, he stressed the need for inculcating a scientific temper among the people enabling them to derive maximum benefits of the advancements taking place in all sectors of science and technology, he said –

> *Development must mean the development of the society. Science and technology have a key role in that development. Panditji talked about developing a scientific temper. The question I should like to ask is: Have we developed that scientific temper or have we developed certain laboratories with certain highly trained scientists? They are two completely different things. It is only if we first develop that temper that we shall develop the scientists who will grow out of that temper. And we must target not only at the top esoteric places but also at the bottom and build from there.*

Rajiv Gandhi often stressed that scientific temper must permeate down to the village level to make them fully aware about the new developments taking place in science & technology and that should equip them to face the challenges of eradicating poverty. Science has been regarded as a powerful instrument of social change. He further said, on creating scientific awareness, while inaugurating the exhibition on New Biology on 14 November 1986 that –

> *Panditji's main thrust when he looked to the future of India and the world was on science and on children, as the two strengths which could take our country to face the challenges of the future. We have from that early beginning, developed our sciences to a very high degree. Today, in certain fields, India is right there at the forefront with the leading nations and we are proud that we have achieved this. We know that we could not have achieved without the foundation that Panditji had laid almost forty years ago. Panditji had talked of a scientific temper and interest in science, in logical thinking, in reasoning and no bigotry or superstition. We still have to reach this scientific temper down to the grassroots in our country, and that is why, we have taken up this major challenge with a new education policy. We hope we will be able reach out to every corner of the country to build this scientific temper, to prepare our youth for the challenges that face them ahead.*

He expressed the need for building public understanding of science and technology for speeding up the process of overall socio-economic development in India on 1st March 1987 at IXth International Congress of Plastic Surgery, New Delhi. He said that–

> *India has an old tradition of Science. 'We had developed a vibrant scientific temper thousands of years ago. Unfortunately, with time, much of it has been lost and we are trying to revive that. Now, as part of the task of nation building, we once again try to rebuild that scientific temper, that openness of mind. We look to the past for inspiration. We look abroad to other countries for interaction, and cross-fertilization of ideas but essentially it is our own efforts.*

References

1. Rajiv Gandhi —Conference on Science and Technology in India: Retrospect and Prospect, New Delhi, 13 November 1985.
2. — Speech in the Lok Sabha, 10 April 1986.
3. — 74th Session, Indian Science Congress Association, Bangalore, 3 January 1987.
4. — 76th Session, Indian Science Congress Association, Madurai, 3 January 1989.
5. — Lok Sabha Debate, 10 April 1986. cc 408.
6. — 74th Session, Indian Science Congress Association, Bangalore, 3 January 1987.

3.6 Protecton of the Environment

Rajiv Gandhi was deeply concerned about the problem of environmental degradation and its catastrophic impact on human civilization. He, thus, whole-heartedly worked for the protection and conservation of the environment and was eager to bring about a halt to its degradation. He said –

> *Another difficult area is that of the environment. When we talk of better productivity in the fields, it is related very much to what is happening with the whole environment. It is not just a question of the amount of forest we have which determines the amount of moisture that is available, but also the pollutants that are thrown into the atmosphere, into water, into land, which affect the health of the crop, not to speak of the health of the people. We need a major thrust and we will be coming out soon with certain laws, which, we hope will make it easier to procure the ecological and environmental balance.*[1]

He further said that -

> *Protecting the environment is very much part of this effort. India has special problems because of the sheer size of our population. The pressure that population puts on the environment is perhaps more in India than in any other country. This is compounded by the development process, and by poverty.*
>
> *Industry is not taking the responsibility of protecting the environment from the side effects. This responsibility must be squarely fixed on industry. It is by bringing about an awareness of the dangers of failure or slip that people will accept the extra cost of protection.*
>
> *We have enacted certain laws, which do not allow certain types of industries to come up in certain areas, and we are trying to give a policy direction so that the protected areas will get industries that do not pollute and are clean.*

> *We have incorporated this consideration into the very process of clearance of projects. No project can even start unless it has full environmental clearance. We have also gone a step further and ensured that if a particular forest has to be cut to accommodate a project, an equivalent area is replaced at some other location, preferably near the same area. Our forest cover in India is already much too low.*
>
> *The priorities in pollution must be an integral part of all new technologies that we are developing. The emphasis must be shifting to low pollution industries and also to industries that have less natural resources and cause less damage to our environment.*[2]

Rajiv Gandhi said that a bureaucratic approach cannot work, especially where we are dealing with people, with the social system. He further said - The National Forest Policy is aimed at conserving forests, resurrecting our eco-system and restoring the geographical balance, along with economic development. This is critical to our country. But to India, in its present state, it is even more critical. It is vital for our survival. Most of our training and education (to the foresters) dates back to the British time when the primary aim of a forester was not to conserve and to protect, but to exploit and use the forest. And unless this basic training is changed right at the beginning, we are going to find it very difficult at a later stage to suddenly start convincing the forester that he is going down the wrong route.

The needs of the people from a forest must be met. ... If we do not give that to him, the alternatives he faces are very tough for him, he cannot have a roof over his head, nor can he eat. But, he cannot starve. ... We could try and supply fuel in the area close to forests more efficiently. Perhaps some of the forest produce could be replaced with the help of research or development in a particular direction. ... The Petroleum Ministry is looking at schemes for gas distribution to lessen the demand for firewood.

Conservation is not something that we can force on people. It is something, which we must build into our thinking right from the early stages of education. It is only then, that our children will feel, from deep inside, that it is their duty to conserve and protect what they have inherited and hand it down to the coming generations.

Tribals come under a lot of pressure whenever any forest act is made or whenever a forest conservation measure takes place. We start accusing the tribals of doing all sorts of things in the forests, forgetting that they have lived in these forests for hundreds and thousands of years. And, somehow forests have survived everything that tribals might have done to them. Perhaps the problem is not what the tribals do but we ourselves do in their name. Perhaps some of the troubles are due to a changing social system.[3]

The environment has been a problem when we were in the midst of the last Lok Sabha campaign, we had a very major disaster in Bhopal. It was followed by one or two other leaks, which fortunately were not as bad as Bhopal disaster. We are ready with a very comprehensive legislation, which we will introduce in this session to control all hazardous substances. For the first time, we are legislating in such a manner that an average citizen can take action. It will be a law that the people will be able to operate. Development generates major environmental problems. The consequences of industrialization are global, cutting across political and religious boundaries. There is another boundary that is affected. We must consider whether we have the right to deprive the future generations of their future.[4] He further said -

> *The environment everywhere is jeopardized by the noxious fumes and life-killing wastes of industrial pollution. The poisoning of the rivers and the seas deprives and endangers all of us, all over the world. The accumulation of carbon dioxide in the atmosphere and the threat to the ozone layer put the innocent to as much risk as the polluters themselves.*

Worst of all is the passing on of pollution and environmental hazards beyond one's boundaries. There is no political boundary, which delimits the spread of poisonous gases, no line on a map which radiation cannot cross, no national frontier at which effluents can be turned back.

At one time, environmental issues related mainly to quality of life of the affluent. Today, in developing countries like ours, we are primarily concerned with the lives of the poorest. When village ponds and wells go dry, it is the poor who trek to ever more distant sources for water. When forests are destroyed, it is the poor and their animals who, in the dry season, trudge hundreds of kilometers in search of lands. It is the livelihood of the poor and their and their hopes that shrivel in the arid anguish of drought and are drowned in the raging fury of floods.

It is also the poor who suffer most from pollution. When borne epidemics strike the urban slums, it is the poor who are afflicted by disease and even death. When factories spew harmful gases into the air, it is the workers in the nearby housing colonies, who suffer the cantagion, when industrial units discharge their effluents into the rivers, it is the poor fisher folk, who are deprived of their incomes.

Although they bear the brunt of environmental damage, the poor are themselves little responsible for any of that damage. For centuries they have lived in harmony with nature. The problem is caused by large-scale commercial exploitation, which garners the profits but escapes the consequences. Yet, when laws are passed and rules are made to conserve the environment, the burden falls on those who have gained the least and suffered the most. The people of the forest cannot suddenly be cordoned off from its bounty. Fuel and building materials must be made available at prices they can afford. Shepherds and cow herds must be found alternative pastures or provided fodder. To be effective, conservation must be humane. That is the challenge before us.

A large number of animal and plant species are seriously threatened. Apart from the ethical and aesthetic case for protecting these disappearing species, it is possible answers to unsolved problems of health and survival might be found in the yet undiscovered secrets of these gene pool reserves.

We in India are now developing mechanisms to control pollution and check the deterioration of the environment. We assess the environmental impact of development work so as to harmonize development with the environment. We carry out research and take the result out to the field. We promote environmental awareness among the people. We hope this will lead to greater vision, concern and care in the planning, designing and implementation of development projects. We learn as we go along.

We do not know enough about the impact on the environment of development decisions. We also do not know about how best to offset damage to the environment. There are no easy solutions. Yet we cannot ignore environmental considerations. We have to strive for the optimum mix through increased knowledge and increased awareness.[5]

Rajiv Gandhi strongly put forward a Third world view -point on environmental issues to the UN General Assembly in October 1987, that – Programmes of conservation must address themselves to inequities in the international economic order. The average citizen of the industrialized countries consumes ten times more fossil fuels and minerals than the average citizen of the developed world. The world's resources just cannot sustain such proliferate consumption of energy and materials. Neither can developing countries be denied the right to develop, nor are the world's natural resources sufficient for all to follow the greedy path to growth. To be effective, he stressed, conservation must be humane. "The answer lies in more rational patterns of consumption, more efficient utilization of depletable resources by the developed countries, and more equitable access to these for developing countries. The international community must also address itself to safety measures in high-risk industries", he pointed out, referring to the disasters in Bhopal, Sevaso and Chernobyl.

> *We have to protect the environment in whatever way we can. This is not just a question for the biologists or biological engineering people who work on how to improve seeds, and how to get more trees growing. It is also the responsibility in part of the industry to see that you do not pollute or produce such chemicals in the atmosphere in an area, which is dangerous to the environment in that particular area. Whenever you are doing research on a new product, you must bear in mind that no environmental damage should result from the process you are designing or the product you are designing. We have taken some precautions by passing an Act, which makes it a criminal liability for anyone to do it. The rules will be out soon and perhaps that will put a little more pressure for compliance.*[6]

While there is a general agreement on the broad causes and consequences of environmental degradation, there is need for detailed scientific work on the causative factors of degradation. We also need detailed scientific assessment of the time related advantages of conservation and the time related disadvantages of neglect. National action alone cannot suffice. Problems of development and the environment can only be resolved through cooperative international action.[7]

Conservation is not something that we can force on people. It is something, which we must build into our thinking right from the early stages of education. It is only then that our children will feel, from deep inside, that it is their duty to conserve and protect what they have inherited and hand it down to the coming generations. National programmes must look at the weaker sections and focus on those who bear the heaviest burden and have the least resilience.

If science is essential for development, it is indispensable for sustainable development. The environmental imperative has now fortunately made its mark on the development scene. In many ways, the origins of the recognition of the interface between environment and development can be traced back to Indiraji's keynote address at the Stockholm Conference on the Environment, held in 1972. ... National action alone cannot suffice. Problems of development and the environment can only be resolved through cooperative international action. While inaugurating the Second World Congress on Engineering and Industry on 7 November 1985 in New Delhi, he said –

> *Industry, while chasing profit, does not pay adequate attention to the dangers of particular chemicals. We know that highly toxic chemicals are still carried in drums, in tankers across the country. We have stopped it in our country. But we know that this happens even in developed countries. Industry is not taking the responsibility of protecting the environment from its side effects. This responsibility must be squarely fixed on industry. It is by bringing about an awareness of the dangers of failure or slip that the people will accept the extra cost of protection.*

Water is Progenitor -While inaugurating the exhibition on "Water", organized by the Ministry of Water Resources and the Jawaharlal Nehru Memorial Fund, New Delhi, 14 November 1988, he said –

> *Water is the source of all life and it is one of our most precious natural resources and yet its supply is limited and very finite. It has to be conserved and well managed. Today, it is also endangered by pollution.*

We need to use science and technology in every aspect of finding water, purifying it and using it. In locating it, we have methods of remote sensing. We have now a technology mission for drinking water. To conserve water, we need dams, water-shed management and better utilization wherever it is being used industrially, in agriculture and even in the home. In India, we have not yet touched real recycling of water and that is another area where science and technology can be of help. We need much better management of water at the national level, at the regional level and most of all at the local, municipal, village levels and in the homes.

Improving the efficiency of the utilization of water must now be one of the key areas for us to concentrate on, as also preventing the pollution of our limited water supplies. The lesson that we must learn is that development and the protection of the environment go very much together. If one tries to have development at the cost of the environment, that will be paid at sometime by somebody either from our generation or from the next. The cost of conservation should be billed into whatever we are doing today. We do not have a right to bill it to the next generation.

India, traditionally has believed Man and Nature to be one and inseparable. This has given us an awareness of Nature, a feeling for Nature. In this context, Rajiv Gandhi recited the following verse of Shri Guru Nanak Dev Ji, at the said UN General Assembly on 19 October 1987, that –

Air is the vital force,
Water is the progenitor:
The vast earth is the mother of all.

The verse sums up 'the Indian tradition of respect for nature, respect for all that gives life, and respect for the sources of our well-being on the Earth. (See references on p. 181.)

The Gazette of India

MINISTRY OF LAW AND JUSTICE

(Legislative Department)

New Delhi, the 26th May, 1986/Jyaisth 5, 1908 (Saka)

The following Act of Parliament received the assent of the President on the 23rd May, 1986, and is hereby published for general information:-

THE ENVIRONMENT (PROTECTION) ACT, 1986

No. 29 OF 1986

[23rd May, 1986]

An Act to provide for the protection and improvement of environment and for matters connected there with:

WHEREAS decisions were taken at the United Nations Conference on the Human Environment held at Stockholm in June, 1972, in which India participated to take appropriate steps for the protection and improvement of human environment;

AND WHEREAS it is considered necessary further to implement the decisions aforesaid in so far as they relate to the protection and improvement of environment and the prevention of hazards to human beings, other living creatures,plants and property;

BE it enacted by Parliament in the Thirty-seventh Year of the Republic of India as follows:-

CHAPTER I

PRELIMINARY

Short title, extent and com

1. (1) This Act may be called the Environment (Protection) Act, 1986.

(2) It extends to the whole of India.

(3) It shall come into force on such date as the Central Government may, by notification in the Official Gazette, appoint and different dates may be appointed for different provisions of this Act and for different areas.

Definitions.

2. In this Act, unless the context otherwise requires,-

(a) "environment" includes water, air and land and the inter-relationship which exists among and between water, air and land, and human beings, other living creatures, plants, micro-organism and property;

(b) "environmental pollutant" means any solid, liquid or gaseous substance present in such concentration as may be, or tend to be, injurious to environment;

(c) "environmental pollution" means the presence in the environment of any environmental pollutant;

(d) "handling", in relation to any substance, means the manufacture, processing, treatment, package storage, transportation, use, collection, destruction. conversion, offering for sale, transfer or the like of such substance;

(e) "hazardous substance" means anv substance or preparation which by reason of its chemical or physico-chemical properties or handling is liable to cause harm to human beings other living creatures plants, micro-organism, property or the environment;

(f) "occupier" in relation to any factory or premises means a person who has control over the affairs of the factory or the premises and includes in relation to any substance, the person in possession of the substance;

(g) "prescribed" means prescribed by rules made under this Act.

CHAPTER II

GENERAL POWERS OF THE CENTRAL GOVERNMENT

Power of Central Government to take measures to

3. (1) Subject to the provisions of this Act, the Central Government shall have the power to take all such measures as it deems necessary or experiment for the purpose of protecting and improving the quality of the environment and

protect and improve environment.

preventing, controlling and abating environmental pollution.

(2) In particular and without prejudice to the generality of the provisons of sub-section (1), such measures may include measures with respect to all or any of the following matters, namely:-

(i) co-ordination of actions by the State Governments, officers and other authorities-

(a) under this Act, or the rules made thereunder; or

(b) under any other law for the time being in force which is relatable to the objects of this Act;

(ii) planning and execution of a nation-wide programme for the prevention, control and abatement of environmental pollution;

(iii) laying down standards for the quality of environment in its various aspects;

(iv)laying down standards for emission or discharge of environmental pollutants from various sources whatsoever;

Provided that standardas for emission or discharge may be laid down under this clause from different sources having regard to the qulity or composition of the emission or discharge of environment pollutants from such sources;

(v) restriction of areas in which any industries, operations or process or class of industries, operations or process shall not be carried out or shall be carried out subject to certain safe-guards;

(vi) laying down procedures and safeguards for the prevention of accidents which may cause environmental pollution and remedial measures for such accidents;

(vii) laying down procedures and safeguards for the handling of hazardous substances;

(viii) examination of such manufacturing processes, materlals and substances as are likely to cause environmental pollution;

(ix) carrying out and sponsoring investigations and research relating to problems of environmental pollution;

(x) inspection of any premises, plant, equipment, machinery, manufacturing or other processes. materials or substances and giving, by order, of such directions to such authorities, officers or persons as it may consider necessary to take steps for the prevention, control and abatement of environmental pollution;

(xi) establishment or recognition of environmental laboratories and institutes to carry out the functions entrusted to such environmental laboratories and institutes under this Act;

(xii) collection and dissemination of information in respect of matters relating to environmental pollution;

(xiii) preparation of manuals, codes or guides relating to the prevention, control and abatement of environmental pollution;

(xiv) such other matters as the Central Government deems necessary or expedient for the purpose of securing the effective implementation of the provisions of this Act.

(3) The Central Government may, if it considers it necessary or expedient so to do for the purposes of this Act, by order, published in the Official Gazette, constitute an authority or authorities by such name or names as may be specified in the order for the purpose of exercising and performing such of the powers and functions (including the power to issue directions under section 5) of the Central Government under this Act and for taking measures with respect to such of the matters referred to in subsection (2) as may be mentioned in the order and subject to the supervision and control of the Central Government

and the provisions of such order, such authority or authorities may exercise the powers or perform the functions or take the measures so mentioned in the order as if such authority or authorities had been empowered by this Act to exercise those powers or perform those functions or take such measures.

Appointment of officers and their powers and functions.

4. (1) Without prejudice to the provisions of sub-section (3) of section 3, the Central Government may appoint officers with such designations as it thinks fit for the purposes ot this Act and may entrust to them such of the powers and functions under this Act as it may deem fit.

(2) The officers appointed under sub-section (1) Shall be subject to the general control and direction of the Central Government or, If so directed by that Government, also of the authority or authorities, if any, constituted under sub-seetion (3) of section 3 of any other authorty or officer.

Power to give directions

5. Notwithstanding anything contained in any other law but subject to the provisions of this Act, the Central Government may, in the exercise of its powers and performance of its functions under this Act, issue directions in writing to any person, officer or any authority and such person, officer or authority shall be bound to comply with such directions.

Explanation-For the avoidance of doubts- it is hereby declared that the power to issue directions under this section include the power to direct-

(a) the closure, prohibition or regulation of any industry, operation or process; Or

(b) stoppage or regulation of the supply of electricity or water or any other service.

Rules to regulate environmental pollution.

6. (1) The Central Government may, by notification in the Official Gazette, make rules in respect of all or any of the matters referred to in section 3.

(2) In particular, and without prejudice to the generality of the fore-going power, such rules may provide for all or any of the following matters, namely:-

(a) the standards of quality of air, water or soil for various areas and purposes;

(b) the maximum allowable limits of concentration of various environmental pollutants (including noise) for different areas;

(c) the procedures and safeguards for the handling of hazardous substances;

(d) the prohibition and restrictions on the handling of hazardous substances in different areas;

(e) the prohibition and restrictions on the location of industries and the carrying on of processes and operations in different areas;

(f) the procedures and safeguards for the prevention of accidents which may cause environmental pollution and for providing for remedial measures for such accidents.

CHAPTER III
PREVENTION, CONTROL AND ABATEMENT OF ENVIRONMENTAL POLLUTION

Persons carrying on industry, operation, etc, not to allow emission or discharge of environmental pollutants in excess of the standards.

7. No person carrying on any industry, operation or process shall discharge or emit or permit to be discharged or emitted any environmental pollutant in excess of such standards as may be prescribed.

Persons handling hazardous substances to comply with proceedural safe-guards.

8. No person shall handle or cause to be handled any hazardous sub-stance except in accordance with such procedure and after complying with such safeguards as may be prescribed.

Furnishing of information to authorities and agencies in certain cases.

9. (1) Where the discharge of any environmental pollutant in excess of the prescribed standards occurs or is apprehended to occur due to any accident or other unforeseen act or event, the person responsible for such discharge and the person in charge of the place at which such discharge occurs or is apprehended to occur shall be bound to prevent or mitigate the environmental pollution caused as a result of such discharge and shall also forthwith-

(a) intimate the fact of such occurrence or apprehension of such occurrence; and

(b) be bound, if called upon, to render all assistance, to such authorities or agencies as may be prescribed.

(2) On receipt of information with respect to the fact or apprehension of any occurrence of the nature referred to in sub-section (1), whether through intimation under that sub-section or otherwise, the authorities or agencies referred to in sub-section (1) shall, as early as practicable, cause such remedial measures to be taken as are necessary to prevent or mitigate the environmental pollution.

(3) The expenses, if any, incurred by any authority or agency with respect to the remedial measures referred to in sub-section (2), together with interest (at such reasonable rate as the Government may, by order, fix) from the date when a demand for the expenses is made until it is paid, may be recovered by such authority or agency

from the person ccmcerned as arrears *or* land revenue or of public demand.

Powers of entry and inspection.

10. (1) Subject to the provisions of this section, any person empowered by the Central Government in this behalf shall have a right to enter, at all reasonable times with such assistance as he considers necessary, any place--

(a) for the purpose of performing any of the functions of the Central Government entrusted to him;

(b) for the purpose of determining whether and if so in what manner, any such functions are to be performed or whether any provisions of this Act or the rules made thereunder or any notice, order, direction or authorisation served, made, given or granted under this Act is being or has been complied with;

(c) for the purpose of examining and testing any equipment, industrial plant, record, register, document or any other material object or for conducting a search of any building in which he has reason to believe that an offence under this Act or the rules made thereunder has been or is being or is about'to be committed and for seizing any such equipment, industrial plant, record, register, document or other material object if he has reasons to believe that it may furnish evidence of the commission of an offence punishable under this Act or the rules made thereunder or that such seizure is necessary to prevent or mitigate environmental pollution.

(2) Every person carrying on any industry, operation or process or handling any hazardous substance shall be bound to render all assistance to the person empowered by the Central Government under sub-section (1) for carrying out the functions under that sub-section and if he fails to do so without any reasonable cause or excuse, he shall be guilty of an offence under this Act.

(3) If any person wilfully delays or obstructs any person empowered by the Central Government under sub-section (1) in the performance of his functions, he shall be guilty of an offence under this Act.

2 of 1974 (4) The provisions of the Code of Criminal Procedure, 1973, or, in relation to the State of Jammu and Kashmir, or any area in which that Code is not in force, the provisions of any corresponding law in force in that State or area shall, so far as may be, apply to any search or seizure under this section as they apply to ,any search or seizure made under the authority of a warrant issued under section 94 of the said Code or, as the case may be, under the corresponding provision of the said law.

Power to take sample, and procedure to be followed in connection therewith.

11. (1) The Central Government or any officer empowered by it in this behalf, shall have power to take, for the purpose of analysis, samples of air, water, soil or other substance from any factory, premises or other place in such manner as may be prescribed.

(2) The result of any analysis of a sample taken under sub-section (1) shall not be admissible in evidence in any legal proceeding unless the provisions of sub-sections (3) and (4) are complied with.

(3) Subject to the provisions of sub-section (4), the person taking the sample under sub-section (1) shall

(a) serve on the occupier or his agent or person in charge of the place, a notice, then and there, in such form as may be prescribed, of his intention to have it so analysed;

(b) in the presence of the occupier or his agent or person, collect a sample for analysis;

(c) cause the sample to be placed in a container or containers which shall be marked and

sealed and shall also be signed both, by the person taking the sample and the occupier or his agent or person;

(d) send without delay, the container or the containers to the laboratory established or recognised by the Central Government under section 12.

(4) When a sample is taken for analysis under sub-section (1) and the person taking the sample serves on the occupier or his agent or person, a notice under clause *(a)* of sub-section (3), then,-

(a) in a case where the occupier, his agent or person wil-fully absents himself, the person takmg the sample shall collect the sample for analysis to be placed in a container or containers which shall be marked and sealed and shall also be signed by the person taking the sample, and

(b) in a case where the occupier or his agent or person present at the time of taking the sample refuses to si,gn the marked and sealed container or containers of the sample as required under clause

(c) of sub-section (3), the marked and sealed container or containers shall be signed by the person taking the samples, and the container or containers shall be sent without delay by the person taking the sample for analysis to the laboratory established or recognised under section 12 and such person shall inform the Government Analyst appointed or recognised under section 13 in writing about the wilful absence of the occupier or his agent or person, or as the case may be, his refusal to sign the container or containers.

12. (1) The Central Government may by notification in the Official Gazette,-

(a) establish one or more environmental laboratories;

(b) recognise one or more laboratories or

institutes as environmental laboratories to carry out the functions entrusted to an environmental laboratory under this Act.

(2) The Central Government may, by notification Gazette, make rules specifying-

(a) the functions of the environmental laboratory;

(b) the procedure for the submission to the said laboratory of samples of air, water, soil or other substance for analysis or tests, the form of the laboratory report thereon and the fees payable for such report;

(c) such other matters as may be necessary or expedient enable that laboratory to carry out its functions.

13. The Central Government may by notification in the Official Gazette, appoint or recognise such persons as it thinks fit and having the prescribed qualifications to be Government Analysts for the purpose of analysis of samples of air, water soil or other substance sent fer analysis to any environmental laboratory established or recognised under sub-section (1) of section 12.

Reports of Government Analysts.

14. Any document purporting to be a report signed by a Government analyst may be used as evidence of the facts stated therein in any proceeding under this Act.

Penalty for contravention of the provisions of the Act and the rules, orders and directions.

15. (1) Whoever fails to comply with or contravenes any of the provisions of this Act, or the rules made or orders or directions issued thereuneder, shall, in respect of each such failure or contravention, be punishable with imprisonment for a term which may extend to five years or with fine which may extend to one lakh rupees, or with both, and in case the failure or contravention continues, with additional fine which may extend to five thousand rupees for every day during which

such failure or contravention continues after the conviction for the first such failure or contravention.

(2) If the failure or contravention referred to in sub-section (1) continues beyond a period of one year after the date of conviction, the offender shall be punishable with imprisonment for a term which may extend to seven years.

Offences by companies.

16. (1) Where any offence under this Act has been committed by a company, every person who at the time the offence was committed, was directly in charge of, and was responsible to the company for the conduct of the business of the company, as well as the company, shall be deemed to be guilty of the offence and shall be liable to be proceeded against and punished accordingly: Provided that nothing contained in this sub-section shall render any such person liable to any punishment provided in this Act, if he proves that the offence was committed without his knowledge or that he exercised all due diligence to prevent the commission of such offence.

(2) Notwithstanding anything contained in sub-section (1), where an offence under this Act has been committed by a company and it is proved that the offence has been committed with the consent or connivance of, or is attributable to any neglect on the part of, any director, manager, secretary Or other officer of the company such director, manager. secretarv or other officer shall also deemed to be guilty of that offence and shall be liable to be proceeded against and punished accordingly.

Explanation-For the purposes of this section,-

(a) "company" means anv body corproate and includes a firm or other association of individuals;

(b) "director", in relation to a firm, means a partner in the firm.

Offences by Government Departments.

17. (1) Where an offence under this Act has been committed by any Department of Government, the Head of the Department shall be deemed to be guilty of the offence and shall be liable to be proceeded against and punished accordingly:

Provided that nothing contained in this section shall render such Head of the Department liable to any punishment if he proves that the offence was committed without his knowledge or that he exercise all due diligence to prevent the commission of such offence.

(2) Notwithstanding anything contained in sub-section (1), where an offence under this Act bas been committed by a Department of Government and it is proved that the offence has been committed with the consent or connivance of, or is attributable to any neglect on the part of, any officer, other than the Head of the Department, such officer shall also be deemed to be guilty of that offence and shall be liable to be proceeded against and punished accordingly.

CHAPTER IV
MISCELLANEOUS

Protection of action taken in good faith.

18. No suit, prosecution or other legal proceeding shall lie against the Government or any officer or other employee of the Government or any authority constituted under this Act or any member, officer or other employee of such authority in respect of anything which is done or intended to be done in good faith in pursuance of this Act or the rules made or orders or directions issued thereunder.

Cognizance of offences.

19. No court shall take cognizance of any offence under this Act except complaint made by-

(a) the Central Government or any authority or officer authorised in this behalf by that Government; or

(b) If any person who has given notice of not less than sixty days, in the manner prescribed, of

the alleged offence and of his intention to make complaint, to the Central Government or the authority or officer authorised as aforesaid.

Information, reports or returns.

20. The Central Government may, in relation to its functions under this Act, from time to thne, require any person, officer, State Government or other authority to furnish to it or any prescribed authority or officer any reports, returns, statistics, accounts and other information and such person, officer, State Government or other authority shall be bound to do so.

Members, officers and employees of the authority constituted under section 3 to be public servants 45 of 1860

21. All the members of the authority, constituted, if any, under section 3 and all officers and other employees of such authority when acting or purporting to act in pursuance of any provisions of this Act or the rules made or orders or directions issued thereunder shall be deemed to be public servants within the meaning of section 21 of the Indian Penal Code.

Bar of jurisdiction.

22. No civil court shall have jurisdiction to entertain any suit or proceeding in respect of anything done, action taken or order or direction issued by the Central Government or any other authority or officer in pursuance of any power conferred by or in relation to its or his functions under this Act.

Power to delegate.

23. Without prejudice to the provisions of sub-section (3) of section 3, the Central Government may, by notification in the Official Gazette, delegate, subject to such conditions and limitations as may be specified in the notification, such of its powers and functions under this Act Information reports or returns.

[except the power to constitute an authority under sub-section (3) of section 3 and to make rules under section 25] as it may deem necessary or expedient, to any officer, State Government or other authority.

Effect of other laws

24. (1) Subjecf to the provisions of sub-section (2) the provisions of this Act and the rules or orders made therein shall have effect notwithstanding anything inconsistent therewith contained in any enactment other than this Act.

(2) Where any act or omission constitutes an offence punishable under this Act and also under any other Act then the offender found guilty of such offence shall be liable to be punished under the other Act and not under this Act.

Power to make rules

25. (1) The Central Government may, by notification in the Official Gazette, make rules for carrying out the purposes of this Act.

(2) In particular, and without prejudice to the generality of the foregoing power, such rules may provide for all or any of the following matters, namely:-

(a) the standards in excess of which environmental pollutants shall not be discharged or emitted under section 7;

(b) the procedure in accordance with and the safeguards in compliance with which hazardous substances shall be handled or cause to be handled under section 8;

(c) the authorities or agencies to which intimation of the fact of occurrence or apprehension of occurrence of the discharge of any environmental pollutant in excess of the prescribed standards shall be given and to whom all assistance shall be bound to be rendered under sub-section (1) of section 9;

(d) the manner in which samples of air, water, soil or other sub-stance for the purpose of analysis shall be taken under sub-section (1) of section 11;

(e) the form in which notice of intention to have

a sample analysed shall be served under clause *(a)* of sub-section (3) of section 11;

(f) the functions of the environmental laboratories, the procedure for the submission to such laboratories of samples of air, water, soil and other substances for analysis or test; the form of laboratory report; the fees payable for such report and other matters to enable such laboratories to carry out their functions under sub-section (2) of section 12;

(g) the qualifications of Government Analyst appointed or recognised for the purpose of analysis of samples of air, water, soil or other substances under section 13;

(h) the manner in which notice of the offence and of the intention to make a complaint to the Central Government shall be given under clause *(b)* of section 19;

(i) the authority or officer to whom any reports, returns, statistics, accounts and other information shall be furnished under section 20;

(j) any other matter which is required to be, or may be, prescribed.

Rules made under this Act to be laid before Parliament.

26. Every rule made under this Act shall be laid, as soon as may be after it is made, before each House of Parliament, while it is in session, for a total period of thirty days which may be comprised in one session or in two or: more successive sessions, and if, before the expiry of the session immediately following the session or the successive sessions afore-said, both Houses agree in making any modification in the rule or both Houses agree that the rule should not be made, the rule shall thereafter have effect only in such modified form or be of no effect, as the case may be; so, however, that any such modification or annulment shall be without prejudice to the validity of anything previously done under that rule.

No.3-1/86-FP
Ministry of Environment and Forests
(Department of Environment, Forests & Wildlife)

Paryavaran Bhavan, CGO Complex,
Lodi Road, New Delhi - 110003.
Dated the 7th December, 1988

RESOLUTION
National Forest Policy, 1988

1. PREAMBLE

1.1. In Resolution No. 13/52-F, dated the 12th May 1952, the Government of India in the erstwhile Ministry of Food and Agriculture enunciated a Forest Policy to be followed in the management of State Forests in the country. However, over the years, forests in the country have suffered serious depletion. This is attributable to relentless pressures arising from ever-increasing demand for fuelwood, fodder and timber; inadequacy of protection measures; diversion of forest lands to non-forest uses without ensuring compensatory afforestation and essential environmental safeguards; and the tendency to look upon forests as revenue earning resource. The need to review the situation and to evolve, for the future, a new strategy of forest conservation has become imperative. Conservation includes preservation, maintenance, sustainable utilisation, restoration, and enhancemlent of the natural environment. It has thus become necessary to review and revise the National Forest Policy.

2. BASIC OBJECTIVES

2.1 The basic objectives that should govern the National Forest Policy are the following :-

- Maintenance of environmental stability through preservation and, where necessary, restoration of the ecological balance that has been adversely disturbed by serious depletion of the forests of the country.
- Conserving the natural heritage of the country by preserving the remaining natural forests with the vast variety of flora

and fauna, which represent the remarkable biological diversity and genetic resources of the country.

- Checking soil erosion and denudation in the catchment areas of rivers, lakes, reservoirs in the interest of soil and water conservation, for mitigating floods and droughts and for the retardation of siltation of reservoirs.
- Checking the extension of sand-dunes in the desert areas of Rajasthan and along the coastal tracts.
- Increasing substantially the forest/tree cover in the country through massive afforestation and social forestry programmes, especially on all denuded, degraded and unproductive lands.
- Meeting the requirements of fuelwood, fodder, minor forest produce and small timber of the rural and tribal populations.
- Increasing the productivity of forests to meet essential national needs.
- Encouraging efficient utilisation of forest produce and maximising substitution of wood.

4.4 Diversion of forest lands for non-forest purposes

4.4.1 Forest land or land with tree cover should not be treated merely as a resource readily available to be utilised for various projects and programmes, but as a national asset which requires to be properly safeguarded for providing. sustained benefits to the entire community. Diversion of forest land for any non-forest purpose should be subject to the most careful examinations by specialists from the standpoint of social and environmental costs and benefits. Construction of dams and reservoirs, mining and industrial development and expansion of agriculture should be consistent with the needs for conservation of trees and forests. Projects which involve such diversion should at least provide in their investment budget, funds for regeneration compensatory afforestation.

4.4.2 Beneficiaries who are allowed mining and quarrying in forest land and in land covered by trees should be required to repair and re-vegetate the area in accordance with established forestry practices. No mining lease should be granted to any party, private or public, without a proper mine management plan appraised from the environmental angle and enforced by adequate machinery.

4.5 Wildlife Conservation

Forest Management should take special care of the needs of wildlife conservation, and forest management plans should include prescriptions for this purpose. It is specially essential to provide for "corridors" linking the protected areas in order to maintain genetic continuity between artificially separated sub-sections of migrant wildlife.

4.6 Tribal People and Forests

Having regard to the symbiotic relationship between the tribal people and forests, a primary task of all agencies responsible for forest management, including the forest development corporations should be to associate the tribal people closely in the protection, regeneration and development of forests as well as to provide gainful employment to people living in and around the forest. While special attention to the following :-

- One of the major causes for degradation of forest is illegal cutting and removal by contractors and their labour. In order to put an end to this practice, cqntractors should be replaced by institutions such as tribal cooperatives, labour cooperatives, government corporations, etc. as early as possible.
- Protection, regeneration and optimum collection of minor forest produce along with institutional arrangements for the marketing of such produce;
- Development of forest villages on par with revenue villages;
- Family oriented schemes for improving the status of the tribal beneficiaries; and
- Undertaking integrated area development programmes to meet the needs of the tribal economy in and around the forest areas, including the provision of alternative sources of domestic energy on a subsidised basis, to reduce pressure on the existing forest areas.

4.7 Shifting Cultivation

Shifting cultivation is affecting the environment and producivity of land adversely. Alternative avenues of income, suitably harmonised with the right landuse practices, should be devised to discourage shifting cultivation. Efforts should be made to contain such cultivation within the area already affected, by propagating improved agricultural practices. Area already damage by such cultivation should be rehabilitated through social forestry and energy plantations.

4.8 Damage to Forests from Encroachments, Fires and Grazing

4.8.1 Encroachment on forest lands has been on the increase. This trend has to be arrested and effective action taken to prevent its continuance. There should be no regularisation of existing encroachments.

4.8.2 The incidence of forest fires in the country is high. Standing trees and fodder are destroyed on a large scale and natural regeneration annihilated by such fires. Special precautions should be taken during the fire season. Improved and modern management practices should be adopted to deal with forest fires.

4.8.3 Grazing in forest areas should be regulated with the involvement of the community. Special conservation areas, young plantations and regeneration areas should be fully protected. Grazing and browsing in forest areas need to be controlled. Adequate grazing fees should be levied to discourage people in forest areas from maintaining large herds of non-essential livestock.

4.9. Forest based Industries

The main considerations governing the establishment of forest-based industries and supply of raw material to them should be as follows:

- As far as possible, a forest-based industry should raise the raw material needed for meeting its own requirements, preferably by establishment of a direct relationship between the factory and the individuals who can grow the raw material by supporting the individuals with inputs including credit, constant technical advice and finally harvesting and transport services.
- No forest-based enterprise, except that at the village or cottage level, should be permitted in the future unless it has been fast cleared after a careful scrutiny with regard to

assured availability of raw material. In any case, the fuel, fodder and timber requirements of the local population should not be sacrificed for this purpose.

- Forest based industries must not only provide employment to local people on priority but also involve them fully in raising trees and raw-material.
- Natural forests serve as a gene pool resource and help to maintain ecological balance. Such forests will not, therefore, be made available to industries for undertaking plantation and for any other activities.
- Farmers, particularly small and marginal farmers would be encouraged to grow, on marginal/degraded lands available with them, wood species required for industries. These may also be grown along with fuel and fodder species on community lands not required for pasture purposes, and by Forest department/corporations on degraded forests, not earmarked for natural regeneration.
- The practice of supply of forest produce to industry at concessional prices should cease. Industry should be encouraged to use alternative raw materials. Import of wood and wood products should be liberalised.
- The above considerations will however, be subject to the current policy relating to land ceiling and land-laws.

4.10 Forest Extension

Forest conservation programme cannot succeed without the willing support and cooperation of the people. It is essential, therefore, to inculcate in the people, a direct interest in forests, their development and conservation, and to make them conscious of the value of trees, wildlife and nature in general. This can be achieved through the involvement of educational institutions, right from the primary stage. Farmers and interested people should be provided opportunities through institutions like Krishi Vigyan Kendras, Trainers' Training Centres to learn agrisilvicultural and silvicultural techniques to ensure optimum use of their land and water resources. Short tenn extension courses and lectures should be organised in order to educate farmers. For this purpose, it is essential that suitable programmes are propagated through mass media, audio-visual aids and the extension machinery.

4.11 Forestry Education

Forestry should be recognised both as a scientific discipline as well as a profession. Agriculture universities and institutions dedicated to the development of forestry education should formulate curricula and courses for imparting academic education and promoting post-graduate research and professional excellence, keeping in view the manpower needs of the country. Academic and professional qualifications in forestry should be kept in view for recruitment to the Indian Forest Service and the State Forest Service. Specialised and orientation courses for developing better management skills by in service training need to be encouraged, taking into account the latest development in forestry and related disciplines.

4.12 Forestry Research

With the increasing recognition of the importance of forests for environmental health, energy and employment, emphasis must be laid on scientific forestry research, necessitating adequate strengthening of the research base as well as new priorities for action. Some broad priority areas of research and development needing special attention are:-

(i) Increasing the productivity of wood and other forest produce per unit of area per unit time by the application of modern scientific and technological methods.

(ii) Revegetation of barren/marginal/waste/mined lands and watershed areas.

(iii) Effective conservation and management of existing forest resources (mainly natural forest eco-systems).

(iv) Research related to social forestry for rural/tribal development.

(v) Development of substitutes to replace wood and wood products.

(vi) Research related to wildlife and management of national parks and sanctuaries.

4.13 Personnel Management

Government policies in personnel management for professional foresters and forest scientists should aim at enhancing their professional competence and status and attracting and retaining qualified and motivated personnel, keeping in view particularly the ardous nature of duties they have to perform, often in remote and inhospitable places.

4.14 Forest Survey and Data Base

Inadequacy of data regarding forest resources is a matter of concern because this creates a false sense of complacency. Priority needs to be accorded to completing the survey of forest resources in the country on scientific lines and to updating information. For this purpose, periodical collection, collation and publication of reliable data on relevant aspects of forest management needs to be improved with recourse to modern technology and equipment.

4.15 Legal Support and Infrastructure Development

Appropriate legislation should be undertaken, supported by adequate infrastructure, at the Centre and State levels in order to implement the Policy effectively.

4.16 Financial Support for Forestry

The objectives of this revised Policy cannot be achieved without the investment of financial and other resources on a substantial scale. Such investment is indeed fully justified considering the contribution of forests in maintaining essential ecological processes and life-support systems and in preserving genetic diversity. Forests should not be looked upon as a source of revenue. Forests are a renewable natural resource. They are a national asset to be protected and enhanced for the well-being of the people and the Nation.

National Water Policy

The year 1987 -88 witnessed adoption *of* the National Water Policy which constitutes a major landmark in the development of water resources in India.

1.2 The National Water Resources Council, under the chairmanship of the Prime Minister, adopted the National Water Policy on 9th September, 1987. Recognising water as a precious national asset, the Policy embodies the nation's resolve that planning and development *of* water resources would be governed by national perspectives. The policy recognises drainage basin as the basic unit of planning for water resources development and calls for appropriate measures to optimise utilisation *of* these resources not only for the benefit of the people living in the basin, but also for transfer *of* surplus waters to meet the requirements *of* water-short areas. The principal elements *of* the policy are recounted below:

(i) Water is a precious national resource and its development should be governed by national perspectives.

(ii) The available resources, both surface and groundwater, should be made utilisable to the maximum extent.

(iii) The unit of planning should be a hydrological unit such as a drainage basin or sub-basin. Appropriate organisations should be established for planned development and management of the river basins.

(iv) Water should be made available to water-short areas by transfer from other areas including transfers from one river basin to another, after taking into account the requirements of the areas, basins.

(v) Project planning for development of water resources should, as far as possible, be for multiple benefits based an integrated and multi-disciplinary approach having regard to human and ecological aspects and special needs of disadvantaged sections of the society.

(vi) In water allocation. ordinarily first priority should be for drinking water with irrigation. hydro-power. industrial and other uses following in that order.

(vii) The groundwater potential should be periodically reassessed and its exploitation regulated with reference to recharge possibilities and considerations of social equity.

(viii) Due care should be taken right from the project planning stage to promote conjunctive use of surface water and groundwater.

(ix) Maintenance modernisation and safety of structures should be ensured through proper organisational arrangements.

(x) There should be close integration of water use and land-use policies and distribution of water should be with due regard to equity and social justice.

(xi) Efficiency of utilisation should be improved in all the diverse uses of water and conservation consciousness promoted through education, regulation, incentives and disincentives.

(xii) Water rates should be such as to foster the motivation for economy in water use and should cover maintenance and operation charges and a part of the fixed cost of hydraulic projects.

(xiii) Farmers should be progressiyely involved in the management of irrigation systems.

(xiv) In flood control and management, the strategy should be to reduce the intensity of floods by sound watershed management and provision of adequate flood cushion in water storage projects wherever feasible. There should be a master plan for flood control and management of each flood-prone basin.

(xv) Land erosion by sea or river should be minimised by suitable cost-effective measures. Indiscriminate occupation of, and economic activity in coastal areas and flood plain zones should be regulated.

(xvi) Needs of drought-prone areas should be given priority in planning water resources development projects. These areas should be made less vulnerable through soil moisture conservation measures, water harvesting practices, development of ground water potential and transfer of surface water where feasible. Less water-demanding modes of development such as pastures and forestly should be encouraged in these areas.

(xvii) A national information system on water resources should be established with a net-work of data banks and data bases integrating and strengthening the existing Central and State level agencies.

(xviii) Training and research efforts should be intensified as integral parts of water resources development programmes.

References

1. Silver Jubilee Convocation, Indian Agricultural Institute, New Delhi, 6 February 1986.
2. Rajiv Gandhi —Second World Congress on Engineering and Environment, New Delhi, 7 November 1985.
3. — 21st Meeting of the Central Board of Forestry, New Delhi, 2 January 1986.
4. — World Commission on Environment and Development, New Delhi, 6 July 1987.
5. — UN General Assembly on Environment and Development, New York, 19 October 1987.
6. — 76th Session, Indian Science Congress Association, Madurai, 3 January 1989.
7. — Conference of the Directors of National labs of CSIR, 28 May 1986.

3.7 COMPUTER REVOLUTION IN INDIA

Rajiv Gandhi's name is synonymous with the ushering of computer revolution in the country. The first policy he announced after taking over as the Prime Minister of India, on 19 November, 1984 was the computer Policy earning him the label of a man who would take India into the 21st century. As a result, import duties were slashed, excise duties were reduced and licensing was liberalized.

Rajiv Gandhi was one of the very few politicians who recognized the importance of technological changes taking place in information technology and made us aware of its impact and prepared us for this massive development. He switched on to the computer age. It was realized that Information Technology is the vehicle, which will take India to the 21st century. Computerization programme was initiated in Railways, Income Tax and many other Government departments. Computers became a part of the school curriculum and the National Council of Educational Research and Training (NCERT) went full steam ahead with computer literacy programme in schools. His initiatives resulted in the setting up of

- Centre for the Development of Telematics (C-DOT).
- Telecom Commission.
- Mahanagar Telephone Nigam Limited (MTNL) for Bombay and Delhi.
- Centre for the Development of Advanced Computing Applications (C-DAC).

He was instrumental in providing India a Super Computer, installed at India Meteorological Department (IMD), New Delhi for numerical prediction of medium range weather forecasting – the accuracy of which is essential for agriculture, civil aviation and cyclone warning activities in the coastal areas of India and the neighbouring countries. *India missed the industrial revolution, it cannot afford to miss the computer revolution, believed Rajiv Gandhi, who pioneered India's high-tech revolution.*

TEXT OF THE COMPUTER POLICY
Announced by the Union Government of India On 19 November 1984

The Government of India have had under consideration the question of reviewing the existing policy for manufacture, import and export of computers and computer-based systems. As a first step in that direction, the following revisions are made to the existing policy and procedures for manufacture, import and export of computers and computer-based systems.

The revision is broadly aimed at accomplishing the following basic objectives:

(i) Enable manufacture in the country of computers based on the latest technology, at prices comparable with international levels and progressively increase indigenisation consistent with economic viability.

(ii) Simplify existing procedures to enable users to obtain computers of their requirements either from indigenous sources or from overseas sources mainly regulated through fiscal resources.

(iii) Promote appropriate applications of computers which are of development - catalysing nature with due regard for long-term benefit of computerization to the country as a whole.

The revised policy and procedures given below pertain to computers and their associated sub-systems like peripherals and software and computer-based systems in which the computer is a major sub-system.

A. *Manufacture*

1. All regulatory measures concerning manufacture like scrutiny of applications for Letters of Intent, Industrial Licences, Foreign Collaboration, Phased Manufacturing Programmes (PMP) and CG and Raw-material imports, will be exercised by the existing Inter-Ministerial Standing Committee (IMSC)

under the Department of Electronics (DOE), which has been designated for this extended purpose. The Computer - Communication and Instrumentation (CCI) Wing of the Department of Electronics will continue to be the Secretariat for this Committee. All applications should also be made directly to the CCI-Wing of DOE.

2. Manufacture of micro / mini computers including personal computers, micro computers and VLSI-based mini - computers including those based on 32-bit chips or equivalent (excluding 32 and higher bit super mini / mainframe architecture) will be permitted to any Indian company, i.e., wholly owned Indian companies and companies having foreign equity not exceeding 40 per cent, in the private or public sector.
3. The manufacture of CPU of mainframes and super mini-computers will be reserved for a period of two years for manufacture by the public sector. The precise definition of Mainframe range of computers and super mini-computers will be laid down from time to time by DOE.
4. A new classification "Computer and Computer-based Systems" will be introduced for the items covered under this policy. This new classification will be entitled for entitlement allowance and other incentives available for new industries. Software development and manufacture is classified as "industry" . The industry will be exempted from the purview of the location policy, etc. in view of its specialized high technology nature.
5. The existing capacity restrictions on the organised sector relating to total production value of Rs. 2 crores per year and of five systems per year belowRs. 3 lakhs will be deleted. Manufacture of micro and mini-computer systems will be permitted without any restriction on capacity except a minimum requirement of a viable capacity and a phased manufacturing programme (PMP), which will result in manufacture with as high indegenisation as is economically viable. The PMP for progressive realization of economically indegenisation as well as progressive updating of technology would be ensured by the Department of Electronics through the IMSC.

6. For companies supplying CPUs Peripherals and other subsystems on original equipment manufacture (OEM) basis liberal import of know-how shall be permitted and the excise duty will be kept at relatively low level with appropriate set - off.
7. A price purchase preference to Public Sector enterprises for Government and public sector purchase of computers would be available as per prevailing Government policies applicable to this sector.
8. For Research and Development units recognized by DOE, import of designs and drawings will be allowed on OGL.
9. Adequately liberal import of designs and drawings, systems software and utility software will be initially permitted for manufacture and later regulated by PMP and raw material clearance. All applications for such imports should be sent to the CCI-Wing of the Department of Electronics and will be examined by the IMSC.
10. The Department of Electronics through IMSC will take appropriate measures for the promotion of standardization around certain LSI / VLSI chips and peripherals with due regard to indigenously made products.
11. Import of software, where allowed, shall be preferably in the form of source code. Special encouragement will be given to central purchase of source code of software and distribution within the country.
12. To be able to manufacture the final product at internationally competitive prices, it is necessary that components should be made available to manufacturers at as near international prices as possible. Suitable revision of the duty structure on components will be recommended by the Department of Electronics trom time to time based on the following principles. Components which are not being manufactured in the country and which are not expected to be manufactured in the near future, will be identified and permitted to be imported at very low levels of import duty. For other components which are manufactured in the country or can be manufactured within a short period, liberal manufacturing facilities will be allowed to be set up taking advantage of

economies of scale. Such components will be protected from imports with sufficiently high protective duty. Such duty structures will be recommended from time to time by the Department of Electronics to the Ministry of Finance.

13. The procedure of import of raw materials and components for actual use of the manufacturer would be simplified and expedited. Up to a specified time limit after the registration of import application with the Department of Electronics, the clearance of raw materials will be governed by the IMSC, which shall give a decision within two months of the registration of the application.

14. Computers manufactured in the country will be protected from imports through fiscal measures like high protective import duty levels recommended by DOE through the IMSC I from time to time. Recommendations wiH be made to the Ministry of Finance to progressively reduce the import duties in order to encourage reduction in the cost of indigenous manufacture.

15. Procedure will be evolved by DOE through IMSC for making indigenous manufacturers competitive with respect to imports by educational institutions, R & D organisations, Defence establishments, other and categories of organisations for which direct import of computers do not attract import duty.

16. A letter of approval will be cancelled if the party does not take effective steps within a period stipulated by the DOE through IMSC.

17. All local manufacturers would be encouraged to provide capability for bilingual (Hindi and English) input-output facility in the computers manufactured by them from 1986 onwards to meet the demand from those who are required to use Hindi under the Official Languages Act.

18. Promotion of applications of computers in any social or economic sector will be carried out by encouraging setting up of System Engineering Companies in the public and private sector without undue constraint as long as the computers and computer sub-systems are bought from indigenous sources as available.

19. Within the ambit of the above-mentioned policy framework all details of procedures will be laid down by the DOE through

the IMSC from time to time. The DOE through the IMSC is also empowered to steer the implementation and interpret the policies and procedures from time to time

B. *Import*

1. The same Inter-Ministerial Standing Committee (IMSC) under the DOE referred to in A(1) will examine the applications for import of computers including import for facilitating software exports. For this latter purpose, IMSC will also have a representative of Commerce Ministry as a Member. All applications should be directly sent to the CCI Wing of the DOE.
2. Import of computers, computer-based systems and computer sub-systems like peripherals for integrating with an imported CPU will be permitted only to actual end users.
3. With liberalization of domestic manufacture, domestic computers will be enabled progressively to compete with imported computers on which a sufficiently high protective import duty will be levied.

   Actual users will be permitted to import standardized EDP systems as complete systems costing less than Rs. 10 lakhs c.i.f. on the basis of liberal procedures by paying a sufficiently high protective duty. This will become effective on 1st April, 1985 when the duty rate will also be announced.
4. For import of computers and predominantly computer -based systems costing more than Rs. 10 lakhs c.i.f. the actual user would be required to apply to the Department of Electronics who would examine the application from the point of desirability of applications, essentiality and indigenous availability.

   If the use of the computer is desirable and is not available indigenously, the user will be permitted to import at a low level of duty from a standardized list which would be announced periodically by the Department of Electronics. This list would contain between 12 and 18 models and will be periodically updated. The standardized list will be maintained to enable the advantage of bulk purchase and facilitate maintenance and exchange of software. To take advantage of the substantial reduction of foreign exchange for bulk purchase, the Department of Electronics would negotiate with the vendors of the models in the standardized list and execute a rate contract where possible, for a fixed duration of time.

5. Where import of computers or computer sub-systems are needed as part of a justified proprietary purchase, or as any special purpose computer not available from indigenous sources, clearance of the Department of Electronics is necessary. A low level of duty would apply.
6. After the clearance has been given by the Department of Electronics for purchase under (4) or (5) above, the user would be free to negotiate directly and take all further procurement action.
7. If for some justifiable special reason, the user wishes to avail of DOE's assistance in the actual procurement of the computer, he may approach DOE for the purpose and come to a proper understanding with the DOE on how the computer is to be procured.
8. Import of application software not available commercially in the country would be permitted to actual users with low duty levels on a case-to-case clearance by DOE. The actual user may avail of OGL facility with a sufficiently high protective import duty for any software after informing the Department of Electronics. In addition, where possible, DOE would arrange for centralized import of software for distribution to manufacturers and users on a no-profit no-loss basis.
9. Maintenance of imported computers and predominantly computer-based systems imported will be done either inhouse by the actual user or by the CMC Limited or by any other agency designated by DOE. The DOE designated agency or CMC or the user responsible for the maintenance of the imported computer systems, will be permitted to import spares, tools, test equipment and software support for warranty maintenance on the basis of CCP licence if so required.
10. All import applications will be processed by the DOE through IMSC within two months of the registration of application in

the CCI Wing of DOE in complete form as per performa notified from time to time.

11. All actual users who have imported computers or purchased indigenous ones who are required to use Hindi under the Official Languages Act, will be encouraged to augment their computing facilities for input-output processing of data in Devnagri in addition to English within two years of installation of the system or within two years from the date of this Notification, whichever is earlier.

12. Within the ambit of the above mentioned policy framework, all details of procedures will be laid down by the DOE through the IMSC from time to time. The DOE through the IMSC is also empowered to steer the implementation and interpret the policies and procedures from time to time.

C. *Software Development and Export*

1. The Department of Electronics will set up an extensive research, design and development facility. This organization will be given special encouragement to not only develop know-how through indigenous efforts, but also import know-how on a centralized basis where found advantageous and absorb as well as improve on this know-how on a continuous basis. This organization would cumulate a standardized menu of know-how for making them available to interested users and entrepreneurs.

2. DOE will set up a Software Development Promotion Agency to give an impetus to the growth of manpower intensive software development efforts for both exports and local requirements including import substitution as an integrated effort.

3. Effective software export promotion on a sustained basis can be effective in the long run only if it is planned as a part of an overall software promotion scheme covering both export and internal requirements including import substitution. Also, planning for software development is integrally connected with the plan for hardware development and system engineering. The Software Export Promotion Policy of January 1982 will continue to apply but will include the following modifications:

(i) The general structure of 100 percent export schemes applied as hitherto, will continue to be applicable for computer items.

(ii) Category 'A' and 'B' scheme will be modified as outlined as in the Import-Export Policy, April 1984 - March 1985, Volume I, Chapter 5, para 22.

(iii) Category 'c' in the existing Software Export Scheme will continue in its present from except from the following additional provisions:

(a) The following two options will be available to the exporter:

(i) either complete duty exemption with customs bonding,

(ii) or, duty payment without custom bonding.

(b) 50 per cent of export earning will be available to the exporter on the same basis as for categories 'A' and 'B'.

(c) All facilities and incentives available under the 100 percent software expot scheme will be available to category 'C' scheme also.

(iv) Software exports shall also be promoted through satellite based data linked with overseas computers. This will be carried out by DEO in coordination with the Ministry of Communication P&T Department.

(v) The National Computer Network, INDONET, will be made available predominantly to promote software export from public and private sector enterprises with special consideration for software house in the small-scale sector.

(vi) For import Computers under any of the software export scheme, a special low duty window will be provided.

D. *Implementation*

1. All the revised policies and procedures outlined above come into effect immediately on the date of issue of this Press Note.
2. Import of computers on the basis outlined in B (3) above will come into force with the announcement of the Import and Export Policy for the period April 1985, March 1986.
3. Notifications concerning specific duty levels applicable until further notice from Ministry of Finance will be issued by them separately.

4. All cases governed by policies and procedures outlined above which are still awaiting notifications in various Government Departments on specific issues will be processed by DEO in the interim as per present policies and procedures.

3.8 Electronics and Telecommunication

We have special problems in the country. The geographical region, the range of telecom demands, from various income groups, from various sections of our society. We cannot deliver these demands unless we start thinking in that original manner, get down to what we really need in the country, and from that, build what will be suitable for India, *said* Rajiv Gandhi, on 3rd February 1987, at the National Conference on Telecommunication Mission. New Delhi.

Electronics is today an agency for the development of perhaps almost every sector of our growth. Electronics is ushering in a new post-industrial revolution. We missed the first one. We cannot miss the second one. Electronics and Telecom are the tools for our development today. ... they can develop with competition, with a very aggressive attitude on the part of everyone involved. ... for real development in the industry, we have to look for more than just custom duty cuts and excise duty reductions. We have to see that industry too rises to the occasion. There is ample scope for rationalization of production lines, better product mixes, improved technologies, perhaps most of all better management in our industries. A sheltered market with too much protection has led to shoddy goods and no real development in the industry.

... What the consumer will need at any given point is a judicious mix of our technology, with certain amounts of imported technology. But we must look at imported technology as a stepping-stone for our own better technology and development, and not as an end to the production process. For such a fast growing and fast changing industry, we will need a tremendous dynamism within the industry, equally within the government departments. Only then shall we be able to adjust as technology develops. ... we have to change this basic attitude. ...one of the ways that we are looking at for bringing about a rise in telecom is through the Telecom Mission.[1] Rajiv Gandhi Said :-

The industrial Revolution led to a gap between the developed and the developing countries. The information

> *revolution today is enlarging that gap. ... That is why it is all the more important that for communication and information technology, we take a leap forward ... to get on to the front-line technology. ... I have no doubt that with the know-how, that we have, we can show the developed countries that Indians can come up, can beat them at their own game, compete with them in their own areas.*
>
> *...We will have to take a leap forward, get on to the front-line technology. Today, we have no doubt that our technologists, our scientists have the capability for this leap. It is for us in Government, for the departments, for all the organizations that are involved in this exercise, to make that leap possible and that will mean a lot of new thinking right down the line, a more aggressive thinking, a more objective thinking, not accepting everything we are given.*[2]

Effective communication performs two important tasks. It brings people together. It is vital for optimizing the management of administrative institutions and growth and developmental programmes. For optimum management, we need rapid collection, collation and transmission of information. Effective telecommunications are a powerful tool in nation building. They are a tool in fostering the speed of new ideas, in dramatically altering the concepts of time and distance. They are vital to the transformation of traditional societies into modern practices. They are indispensable for involving and getting the people to participate in national policies and programmes. And it is for this reason that we have given such high priority to telecom in our developmental programmes.

... your accomplishments (C-DOT's) demonstrate the possibility and the potential of developing new technologies which are geared to our particular needs and which are suited to our environment. This shows what developing countries can achieve in sophisticated areas like telematics. ... For the first time, we have seen (rural exchanges) equipment designed for our own conditions, our own situations where we do not have to put up very expensive air-conditioned, clean-air units to run normal equipment, where maintenance can be done from a distance are standardized so that with just a few selected components, you can have quick efficient maintenance. ... Following C-DOT's success in indigenous digital switching technology, the next challenge is the technology for digital transmission. ... C-DOT can thus make a lasting contribution not just to telecommunication, but also to the ethos in the government departments and they can bring about a new work culture, new work standards, new environment, new accountability and it can be an example to all our R & D facilities. ... This requires leap-frogging that gap. This is possible only with self-confidence in our ability, in a single mindedness in pursuing our goal. It is possible with a highly motivated leadership, at every level and in every institution, and most of all with dedicated hard work.[3]

> *We have geared our objectives to our needs. Our overall target is to put the entire population of 800 million to within five minutes walking distance of the telecom. It is a very ambitious target and a number of unique steps would have to be taken, taking our environment and these needs into consideration. ... We would like greater access to the rural areas by satellites. We needed to put all these together and we have done that in a Telecom Mission – an integrated national network, which will give increased accessibility to all and special attention to the more remote and rural areas.*[4]

On realizing that educated manpower is going to be the greatest asset of a nation in the merging world economy, he advocated the need for human resource development in electronics and telecommunication. He said at the Seminar on Investment Opportunities in Electronics, on 21 February 1985 that –

> *To get electronics really moving in India, we have to go down to other end of the chain. We are mostly talking about manufacturing and selling. We have to go to the other end and produce enough people who will*

be able to deal with the equipment that you are about to produce, which means a turnaround in our education system. We need many more institutes like this, but oriented and run in a much more professional manner, oriented towards more modern fields of technology. We need to really develop a mentality in our people of using modern methods.

He stressed that R & D should be undertaken with a view to exploring new vistas and attaining excellence in the field. He was against providing license protection or import duty concessions to the Indian electronics industry, as it would curb the spirit of competition, as well as, zeal of doing innovations. To quote him further –

Electronics in India has been developed by the small scale sector and by the public sector. We have got a very large gap in between. We would like to fill this gap. But while filling this gap, we shall try and see that the present industry is protected, not completely but to some extent. "We have been looking at these for the past couple of years. We came out with a completely new package for the electronics industry some months ago, and I think you will like the package that we shall present you in the next session of Parliament. But I would like to point out that many of the concessions that we gave, many of the reductions in controls, have not been passed on to the consumers in the way that they should have been. The industry has not been as dynamic as it should have been. Well, we shall give you another chance. If it does not work, we shall have to think of prodding a little harder, not by force but by some other means. I feel, for example, that protection should be of only one sort, preferably only fiscal protection and not license protection, which means that you will have to be more efficient. You will have to compete.

While stressing the need for attaining self-reliance in electronics and telecommunications, Rajiv Gandhi envisioned targeting beyond self-reliance, that is, working towards the attainment of peaks of excellence in the world market. In this context, he further stated that – India has made tremendous progress in just about every area of telecommunication. In developing telecommunications, we have kept the watchword of self-reliance, not self-sufficiency but self-reliance. Self-reliance does not mean an autarky, but rather seeking cooperation from others while avoiding dependence by emphasizing our own technology and indigenous manufacture. We have, therefore, stressed Research and Development and product development.

One of the most important aspects of the telecom industry or the electronics industry is that we must become self-reliant. It is not enough to keep looking for important concessions and keep asking for protection. At the 30th Technical Convention of the Institute of Electronics and Telecommunication Engineers on 16 January 1987, he said –

> *Self-reliance will have to be the key. You have raised some very valid points about the volume of production and the price of goods. We shall have to study these to see how we can give enough volume of production to satisfy the requirement of R & D, which is essential. There is today almost no real R & D being done within the country. We must not fall into the trap of mere imitative research. This is what I meant when I said there was no real R & D because with some exceptions, our investment in R & D is in terms of replacing what has already been discovered and invented and manufactured elsewhere by something of our own. This is important, but what is more important is to take that qualitative jump into real front-line thinking. This is still not taking place, the way it should be in India.*
>
> *We have chased other people's discoveries for forty years and we have built a foundation for own development. It is time that we change over and try*

to become world leaders in certain specific areas and then in much broader fields. To become world leaders, we shall have to become a coveted source of supply for others, which mean very high quality standards, very high management levels, very good delivery schedules. Again, we are not up to the mark. Reliability is not good enough. Human engineering is still something that our engineers do not even dream about. It is still banging things in a box, painting it some colour, and throwing it out and hoping that everything will work from there onwards. But a total design package is not done, to the best of my knowledge, in any product that is truly Indian. We cannot become world leaders if we leave this important area out.

The challenge for us is not to become a world leader in one or two items. That would not be sufficient for a country like India. We must become world leaders across the spectrum. That is the challenge that we must face.

Telecom is one of the key determinants of the growth of an economy of a country today, and perhaps because this has not been fully realized in India that telecom has not got the attention, which was its due. While inaugurating the Asia and Pacific Telecommunication Development Conference on 22 February 1988, Rajiv Gandhi said – Good telecom is vital but it is very capital intensive. We find that developing countries creep along and are not able to move as rapidly as they would perhaps like to. We must take the quantum jump, ignoring the intermediate technologies which will be appropriate for the time when we really come on line with the developed countries.

Rajiv Gandhi's name is synonymous with the ushering of electronics revolution or computer revolution in India. Highlighting this at a seminar on 21 February 1985, he recognized that –

This is a field that interests me and is critical for India's growth. Electronics is really like the nervous system of a nation. As a nation evolves that nervous system must evolve with it, just as it evolved with the species. In the earliest species, there were barely 250 odd nerve-junctions. The humans have 15 billion odd nerve-junctions.

We need a similar network in our country if India is to progress; if India is to move ahead, if we are to keep up with the world. We missed one bus with the Industrial Revolution, a sudden boost in muscle power, and we were not able to catch up for 300 years. May be, we didn't jump on the second bus on time – and that is the electronic revolution or computer revolution – and now we might have to run behind that bus, catch up to it and jump on to it. I think we are capable of doing this.

He further said –

Sometimes our decision-making processes are so slow that by the time we decide to do something we have a totally new technology available and then we start rethinking whether we are going right or not. So, our process will have to be speeded up very much. Our demand for the industry to be innovative in technology must be met by a pledge on both sides to give an equal innovativeness in an adaptable policy which develops, as the systems develop. The Government departments like Railways, Defence, Telecom and the State Governments; all must be encouraged to establish positive thinking in their various fields.

One of the ways that we are looking at for bringing about a rise in telecom is through the Telecom Mission. The mission is not just targeted to change the communication scenario in the country, but to make communication really accessible across the country. From my point of view, what is going to be much more important, is the way the mission is being carried out because, hopefully, that will bring about a new thinking. A new methodology in Government which will meet the dynamism that is needed for industry today.

We must now start looking beyond the electron to the proton. This is the time that India must switch over. We are ready in terms of manpower, in terms of attitude. But a definite thrust is required. I hope, the government departments will be aggressive in this area and not too cautious and will move in while it is still a new area, said Rajiv Gandhi on 16 January 1987 at IETE Convention.

We now see a complete revolution in the use of electronics in India. Electronics industry has flourished well and one can see a variety of personal computers as well as other office automation in most of the public and private sector organizations. The mushroomed growth of IT personnel in India and their contribution to the software industry, within and outside the country, now stands testimony to the vision Rajiv Gandhi of making India proud in the world market.

References

1. Rajiv Gandhi —30th Technical Convention, Institute of Electronics and Telecommunication Engineers, New Delhi, 16 January 1987.
2. — National Conference on Telecom Mission, New Delhi, 3 January 1987.
3. — Presentation of C-DOT's report to the Nation on its First Technology Mission, New Delhi, 1 October 1987.
4. —Asia and Pacific Telecommunication Development Conference, New Delhi, 22 February 1988.

3.9 Alleviation of Poverty

Panditji talked of science and technology when nobody believed that India could really do very much in that direction. There was a tremendous skepticism. You must remember what sort of argument and discussions went on those days about whether we should have a purely khadi industry or a proper modern industry. The fact is that if India is to get out of poverty, to become a developed country, it can only do so by developing science and technology.[1] Rajiv Gandhi further said -

> *Again, it is not enough just to be working at the frontiers of science and technology, we must develop capability of changing that into a useful product to be used by our people. Traditionally, we have not been very good at that in India, but we are trying to change that.*
>
> *We have set up a number of technology missions, which start with the frontiers of science and hopefully will end up in the homes of our people, in their daily lives. If India is to win this struggle against poverty, it is only with the most modern and best methods that we stand a chance.*
>
> *We look forward to you and many other scientists ... to help us in this giant step that country has to take.*[2]

He said, "We have already identified thrust areas where we will concentrate in such a manner as we have done with our space research, our food production, our nuclear research and some other areas. We would like now to broaden that thrust into areas, which are critical to us: energy, oilseeds and certain high technology areas where we need the technology which we are not just able to get from other countries. ...we are today looking towards developing various technologies, whether it is in energy, whether it is in certain areas of food production, oilseeds, whether it is in certain specific defence areas. What we are looking for is to use the most modern technology for the benefits of the poorest and the most depressed in our country.[3] Our task in India is to end poverty. The challenge to our scientists is:

- How can modern scientific and technological knowledge be brought to bear on the task of removing poverty?
- How we can bring our rural, more backward areas not just a step behind the other countries, but equal to the most developed countries?

That challenge has been in front of our scientists in specified fields. They have shown that they can do it. I look forward to our scientists accepting that challenge and bringing India ahead of the most developed countries in certain fields and gradually in all the fields.[3]

We must remember that the primary problem that we face in India is one of removing poverty and keeping in mind, the litmus test for any national activity is how it helps us remove poverty.[4] According to Rajiv Gandhi -

> *The poverty gap is essentially a technology gap. What separates the developed from the developing country is the level of technology that is used directly or indirectly in the everyday lives of our own people. Within a country, what defines and distinguishes the better off from the worse off is again, the quantity and quality of technology that they use in their daily lives.*
>
> *To eliminate poverty, we must improve the technology input at the lower levels of our society. ...We have developed a number of technology missions to carry out just this task, to direct the high technology and scientific development towards removing poverty, and the war on poverty. By putting together all that is required in technology and managerial power and strength, by putting together the best in scientific developments and breakthroughs we can meet the needs of the poor. ... There can be no poverty alleviation without technological upgradation.*[5]

Rajiv Gandhi said in Parliament that - "Our priority is basically the removal of poverty in the rural areas, and the fundamental part of that has to be the development of our agriculture and down stream products from agriculture. We have seen that, with the most advanced technologies, the most scientific developments being applied to agriculture, and related industries, we have achieved a greater revolution in the north-western states. This did not come by ignoring science and technology. It came about by using science and technology at the right point and by using appropriate technology. It came about by using the most advanced and sophisticated technology, biotechnology, genetic technology, use of fertilizers and electricity. And that is what has changed the picture of our rural areas.

... Whether it is a question of broadcasting or telecommunication for better administration, for better productivity or a better assessment of markets for the farmer, whether it is better weather information to help the farmer sow his seeds or help the farmer to protect his crop, it is all technology working for the poorest people in our country."

References

1. Rajiv Gandhi —Conference on Science and Technology in India – Retrospect and Prospect, New Delhi, 13 November 1985.
2. — Conference of the Directors of National Laboratories, CSIR, New Delhi, 28 May 1986.
3. — Valedictory address, 73rd Session, Indian Science Congress Association, New Delhi, 3 January 1986.
4. — Presenting the Shanti Swarup Bhatnagar Award for Science and Technology, New Delhi, 17 October 1988.
5. — Foundation laying function of the Indian National Academy of Engineering, New Delhi, 11 April 1988.
6. — Speech in the Lok Sabha, 10 April 1986.

3.10 Technological Innovation and Industry

There is lot be said for the tender system to see that we get the best deal. But there is lot be said for the tender system in destroying quality, in destroying any sense of excellence or doing things a little better. So basic government thinking has to change. ... Simply things like a public sector captive factory supplying to government, can they get away with giving us rubbish? Can they get away with delays which costs us years? Why does this happen? Because the technology is not good enough. When I talk of technology, I don't mean hard equipment, I am including the worker because he is very much a part of that process. If the worker does not have a scientific temper, he is not going to be able to produce quality; ... we need feedback from the field to see how the components are failing. What are the problems that the users are having? That will then give the direction for research to be done. I don't think there is enough feedback coming in that sense, said Rajiv Gandhi at the Conference on Science and Technology in India – Retrospect and Prospect on 13 November 1985.

Rajiv Gandhi proposed a new strategy for technology upgradation, on 22 March 1985, stating that the government would concentrate on certain areas leaving others to the private sector, so that together key areas in the industry may come up to the international level in about 10 or 15 years. The government would come up with a programme for the purpose hopefully during the current session of the Parliament itself and would like the industry to respond to it, he said while inaugurating a National Conference on Exports, organized by the Association of Indian Engineering Industry (AIEI) on the occasion of its 90th anniversary. He further stated that in certain areas, India could afford to be behind one or two generations in technology. But in others, the fast growing industry, technology must be up-to-date, so that India moves together with the rest of the world.

Development must mean the development of society. Science and technology have a key role in that development. He said in the Lok Sabha on 10 April 1986, that "If a country uses better technology, it is a developed country. If it uses worst or older technology, it is a backward country and an under-developed country. Within our country, the same thing holds true for a backward village in India and Delhi or Bombay. ... That there is only one difference that is the difference in technology they use in their day-to-day lives.[1]"

Still, what is lacking is a demand to improve what we already have imported. If we get a technology for defence or any other front-line technology, we must not be satisfied with just getting it and sitting on it for a twenty or thirty years and suddenly saying – "My God, we have got left behind!" That should only be a stepping stone, a starting point, from which scientists must take up the challenge and catch up and get ahead of other countries in basic research, in basic understanding.

He said - *Today, we are in a position from which we can take this lead in many areas. For much, too long, we have been playing this game of chasing other people's research. It is not good enough. It is not going to work any longer. It has served its purpose during this phase of our development, but that phase is over. Now we must target for front-line research, to try and do what others have already done. We must learn from what we have done, and we must take that jump and get to the front, to the cutting edge of technology. I know that capability is there in our scientists but it requires just that little bit more thrust. ... We are fed up of playing the game of catch-up. We want now to get on to the front-line. We should not be satisfied with second-rate technologies, second-rate development. We must go to the front areas.*[2]

...Technological upgradation is very very important and it must relate to the cost of the products. ... The challenge is to grow with new technologies and not to get caught up at each step. The challenge must be not just to import technology but to indigenise; not indigenise in a retrograde fashion, but indigenise with a view to aggressive growth so that industry does not stagnate but grows from the technology you have brought. The next generation must be ours.[3] He said - *This is the time we must show the world that we can break-through and give the lead in a number of areas. After two centuries of stagnation, we are now on the way to acquiring technological and scientific self-reliance. We have acquired the ability to achieve but are still to fully achieve.*[4] *Our national goal must be self-reliance.* The challenge for us is not to become a world leader in one or two items. That would not be sufficient for a country like India. We must become world leaders across the spectrum. That is the challenge that we must face.[5]

What we need to establish are adequate linkages between science and technology, on the one hand and the economic and productive sectors on the other. Excellence in development oriented science and technology should be our national objective and we need to create an economic environment in which competitive pressures on industry compel industry to turn to R & D for product development, improve quality, and cost efficiency.[6]

Rajiv Gandhi said that - Our industry is today functioning almost entirely on imported technology, may be bought out, may be copied. But how much of our industries are actually functioning of Indian developed technologies? A small fraction. This is what we have got to change. And this will change when there is a basic thrust not just for developing a particular product or trying to improve a product or to substitute a material in a product. We must go down to the manufacturing process or the production process.[7] To quote him further-

Our industries are not going to our universities and wanting research done, wanting improvements. This somehow must happen, we have already given instructions to the public sector units that they must go to universities, they must go to our lab and ask for results. I hope this will begin soon. Similarly we have asked our defence industries to try and reach out to as many institutions as possible to concentrate in their few establishments. Again this will give a new life, a new thrust, to scientific research right across the country.[8]

We have chased other people's discoveries for forty years and we have built a foundation for own development. It is time that we change over and try to become world leaders in certain specific areas and then in much broader fields. To become world leaders, we shall have to become a coveted source of supply for others, which mean very high quality standards, very high management levels, very good delivery schedules. ... Human engineering is still something that our engineers do not even dream about.

The quality of our products is by and large not upto the required standard. An Indian customer has seen the quality of products from other countries, and he is more and more reluctant to accept the quality of Indian products. For export too, the quality is important. Quality cannot be built in just by putting in more quality control or by mere checks. It is the ethos that must permeate the entire process, in the management, in the workers, in the system. But productivity in labour and efficiency in the industry must come with improving the training standards of labour. I feel that too often, in Indian industry, labour is not upgraded over the years; it stagnates with a particular level of technology and then it becomes a vested interest not to upgrade the technology. ... we must break out of this. Training for human development must be a continuous process. It must go on throughout life.[9]

"India had always been at the forefront of science and technology till we were colonized. It was with colonization that our science and technology started falling behind. But in recent years, we have once more seen a revival of that tradition of science and technology and being at the frontiers of knowledge. Today, we also recall the many scientists who have given new life to India's science and technology in recent years, such as Prof. C.V. Raman, Ramanujan, J.C. Bose etc."[10]

> *After forty years of independence, we are today at a phase, in a position where we can reach out. We have developed the expertise, the know-how; the human resources. We have developed the capabilities to put India back into that place. The challenge is now with you.*[11]

Rajiv Gandhi said, at the All India Businessmen's Convention, on 12 March 1986, that – during these past years, we have been more or less content with absorbing technology that has been developed in other countries, getting it over, using it, and educating our people how they can develop by using this technology, either on the shop-floor or on the farm. But I feel the time has come when this basic attitude must change. If India is not to lag behind other countries, then our basic thinking has to change, we should not be thinking of what we can import and then learn from that, but we should identify certain areas, where we will forge ahead, equal to any other country in the world. We can do this and have done this in a number of fields. It needs a will, it needs a determination and it needs certain involvement of all the people who are doing it. Whether in government or out of government, we must work together to achieve this end.

"In the past, our industrialization has been on the policies that the government put forward but basically the target has been to increase the number of jobs, to increase employment, to train our people in very basic talents. We have to achieve a substantial amount here. Today the question of our competitiveness is coming in. Are we being able to cope with the market pressures around the world?"

"What we need is an Indian approach to Indian problems. We should not be looking for a Japanese or an American or a German solution to Indian problems. Let me say that what we would like to give is to have a constructive dialogue on how to develop Indian industry and today we would like every energy that is available in India, in every sector, to be channelised positively in one direction, that of taking India ahead, of bringing it in line with the best in the world and after that aiming for beyond that".

Industrial Development

> *Indian industry today has to catch up with the industry all over the world. In everything that we have done today, except perhaps in a very few limited sectors, we have limited ourselves or satisfied ourselves with buying a certain technology, never attempting to develop that technology and catch up with the people who sold that technology, nor have we gone ahead of the people who sold that technology to us. Most probably, it has not even been attempted. This basic attitude must change. We can identify which sectors we want to handle. But unless we change the attitude, India cannot be anywhere you and I want India to be. If this attitude remains in our people, we will always remain number two, and we do not want to remain number two, whether it is industry or anything else. We have the capability of going ahead equally well like any other country in the world, and we must do that today,* said Rajiv Gandhi on 12 March 1986.

Industry in the past has, no doubt, contributed towards the complete transformation from a stagnant, declining economy to an economy which is becoming more and more dynamic. The challenges ahead are even greater. Our industry has been protected, as I pointed out. We are going through a phase of allowing them to import technology. Unfortunately, our industry has done almost no development of technology. We import technology, we use it and 20 years later we are still using the same technology. We have done no homework of our own. We have done no development of our own, not even in the small sector. Of course, I am talking in general terms. There are certain thrust areas where our science and technology have done tremendous work. In the nuclear field, for example, in space, in certain biotechnology areas. But by and large, our industry has relied too much on importing technology. And because of the protection, they have not bothered to develop technology. Rajiv Gandhi made the above statement at the Silver Jubilee Convocation address to the Indian Institute of Technology, Delhi on 19 December 1985.

While inaugurating the All India Businessmen's Convention, on 12 March 1986, he stressed the need for undertaking R & D in new and emergent fields. He said that –

> *In the past, our industrialization has been on the policies that the Government put forward but basically the target has been to increase the number of jobs, to increase employment, to train our people in very basic talents. We have to achieve a substantial amount here. Today the question of our competitiveness is coming in. Are we being able to cope with the market pressures around the world? We have a very pushy soft market at home. Almost anything that is made is very easily sold. There are no pressures as such and the system that has evolved whether by the industry or by certain politics put forward by the Government has resulted in this easy.*

Technological achievement and attainment of self-reliance, technological development and eradication of poverty, dynamism and competitiveness of Indian industry, production of quality products etc. were the agenda before Rajiv Gandhi. While address the foundation laying ceremony of the Indian National Academy of Engineering at New Delhi on 11 April 1988, he said, he said –

> *It has taken us forty years to catch up to these frontier areas. This is the time that we show the world that we can breakthrough and give the lead in a number of areas. After two centuries of stagnation, we are now on the way to acquiring the technological*

and scientific self-reliance. We have acquired the ability to achieve but we are still to fully achieve. The Academy's duty will be to bridge that gap, between the potential that has been created, between what is achievable and what India must achieve.

References

1. Rajiv Gandhi —Speech in the Lok Sabha, 10 April 1986.
2. — 73rd Session, Indian Science Congress Association, New Delhi, 8 January 1986.
3. — Platinum Jubilee celebrations, South Indian Chamber of Commerce and Industry, Kalaivanar, 27 March 1987.
4. — Foundation laying function of the Indian National Academy of Engineering, New Delhi, 11 April 1988.
5. — 30th Technical Convention, Institute of Electronics and Telecommunication Engineers, New Delhi, 16 January 1987.
6. — 76th Session, Indian Science Congress Association, Madurai, 3 January 1989.
7. — Conference on Science and Technology in India – Retrospect and Prospect, 13 November 1985, New Delhi.
8. — 73rd Session, Indian Science Congress Association, New Delhi, 8 January 1986.
9. — Platinum Jubilee Celebrations, South Indian Chamber of Commerce and Industry, Kalaivanar, 27 March 1987.
10. — Foundation Day Celebration of the CSIR, New Delhi, 20 September 1987.
11. — Foundation laying function of the Indian National Academy of Engineering, New Delhi, 11 April 1988.

Statement on Textile Policy

(June, 1985)

The textile industry has a unique place in the economy of our country. Its contribution to industrial production, employment and export earnings is very significant. This industry provides one of the basic necessities of life. The employment provided by it is a source of livelihood for millions of people, most of whom live in rural and remote areas. Its exports contribute a substantial part of our total foreign exchange earnings. The healthy development and rapid growth of this industry is, therefore, of vital importance.

2. In the past few years, the development of the textile industry has been guided by the policy framework announced in March 1981. While considerable progress has since been achieved in several areas under this policy framework, the objectives of the textile policy outlined in the Textile Policy Statement have not been fully achieved. Thus, the per capita availability for and the per capita consumption of cloth, of our growing population, still remain at a very low level. There is evidence of an increase in the incidence of sickness, particularly in the organised mill sector, reflected in a large number of closed units. There is a large unsatisfied demand for durable synthetic and blended fabrics at cheaper prices which is not being met by indigenous production. The full export potential of textile products remains to be realised.

3. The textile industry has experienced fluctuations in its fortunes in the past also. However, an analysis of the current difficulties faced by the industry reveals that the present crisis of the industry is neither cyclical nor temporary, but suggests deeper structural weaknesses. Therefore, the Government have reviewed the present textile and after careful consideration, have formulated this new policy for the restructuring of the textile industry in India with a longer term perspective.

4. The existing textile policy sets out a number of objectives. While each of these objectives is important, the multiplicity of objectives has inhibited the achievements of the main task of the textile industry, that is to increase the production of cloth of acceptable quality at reasonable prices to meet the clothing requirements of a growing population. Henceforth, the approach to the textile industry would be guided by this main objective. In the

pursuit of this main objective, the employment and export potential of the industry shall be kept in view. The availability of cloth at affordable prices for the poorer sections of the population shall be augmented.

5. The textile industry has, so far, been viewed in a compartmentalised manner either in terms of various sectors namely, organised mills, power looms, and handlooms, or in terms of fibre use namely, cotton textile, woollen textiles, manmade textiles and silk textiles. Classification on such grounds have led to structural rigidities in the textile industry. When the industry tends to be viewed in parts rather than as an integrated whole, it inhibits the technology use and production-flexibility commensurate with the pattern of consumer demand. Such distinctions have led to the application of a policy mix which is sector-specific or fibrespecific resulting in the emergence of special interests on the one hand and fossilisation on the other. To achieve the main objective of the textile policy, it is necessary to eliminate the existing structural rigidities and to evolve a more integrated view of the textile industry.

6. The proposed restructuring of the textile industry would have the following three main dimensions:-

(a) the industry shall be viewed in terms of the stages of its manufacturing process, namely, spinning, weaving and processing;

(b) the industry shall be provided with fuller flexibility in the use of various fibres; and

(c) the industry shall be subject to more pragmatic policies regarding creation or contraction of capacities by units in order to increase competition and promote healthy growth in the industry.

7. In the spinning sector, all steps will be taken to ensure optimum utilisation of the spinning capacity. The availability of raw materials for the spinning sector would be augmented. The infrastructure for the distribution of yarn would be strengthened. At the same time, necessary measures to encourage and increase spinning in the Khadi sector would be taken in view of its large employment potential.

8. In the weaving sector, the distinct and unique role of the handloom sector shall be preserved. The growth and development

of this sector shall receive priority. The composite mills and the powerlooms have their own respective strengths and weaknesses. For the purpose of policy, powerlooms in the organised mill sector and in the unorganised powerloom sector shall, as far as possible, be treated at par and allowed to compete on the basis for their inherent strengths and capabilities.

9. In the processing sector, the independent power processors and the processing houses in the mills would be treated at par and each would be allowed to operate on the basis of its competitive strength. The small hand-processing units with limited output will receive special consideration.

10. The multi-fibre approach implicit in providing fuller fibre flexibility would be guided by the following considerations:-

(i) Full fibre flexibility as between cotton and man-made fibres/ yarn would be provided to the textile industry. Greater fibre flexibility in the use of wool shall be provided in a phased manner to units licensed for cotton and man-made textiles; woollen units shall be given full fibre flexibility;

(ii) Adequate availability of man-made fibres/ yarn at reasonable prices shall be ensured by increased domestic production supplemented as necessary by imports;

(iii) Creation of capacity by new units and expansion of capacity by existing units for production of synthetic fibres/yarn would be so determined as to realise economies of scale in order to reduce costs of production;

(iv) Fiscal levies on man-made fibres yarn and on the intermediates used as inputs for the production of such fibres yarn, shall be progressively reduced in such a manner as to facilitate absorption of increased domestic production so that the benefit flows to the consumer in the form of lower prices of synthetic and blended fabrics; and

(v) The export window shall be kept open for man-made fibres/ yarn.

11. The pre-eminent role of cotton as the main raw material of textile industry would be maintained. Utilisation of indigenous cotton would be ensured by domestic consumption and by export of cotton, yarn and other manufactures. Cotton growers shall always be assured off-take of their produce at remunerative prices. Cotton needed by

the textile industry would be made available in adequate quantity and at reasonable prices. The role and functions of the Cotton Corporation of India would be reformulated to include price stabilisation operations. For this purpose, the Corporation would have the necessary access to international markets. The present varietal imbalance of cotton shall be corrected by a mix of policies aimed at encouraging increased use of long and extra varieties of cotton on the one hand and higher production of short and medium staple varieties on the other.

12. Capacity expansion by existing units and capacity creation by new units would be permitted subject to the general industrial policies including the provision of the MRTP Act and FERA. As a corollary, units would also be allowed to contract capacities, including closure of a unit or part thereof, wherever necessary and justified, provided the interests of the workers are full protected. This approach would increase the degree of competition among units in the industry and create an environment conducive to a reduction in cost and an improvement in quality.

13. The unplanned growth of powerlooms in the unorganised sector has mostly tended to concentrate in a few areas. A significant proportion of the powerlooms remain unregistered and unauthorised. Henceforth, there shall be compulsory registration of all powerlooms. The organisation of production in the powerloom sector should be guided by the objectives of raising productivity, increasing efficiency, improving workers' welfare and facilitating locational dispersal. In keeping with these objectives, a suitable package of measures would be evolved in order to bring about a healthy development of the powerloom sector. It would be ensured that powerlooms do not violate the locational guidelines for industries, particularly in the large cities and metropolise. Effective measures would be taken to see that the powerlooms do not encroach upon article reserved for exclusive production by the Handloom. The organisational set up required for the above purposes shall be strengthened.

14. In order to preserve the unique role of Handlooms and enable them to realise their full potential as also to ensure higher earnings for the handloom weavers, the following main steps shall be taken:-

(i) The development of handlooms through cooperative and

Central/ State level corporations shall be intensified;

(ii) Greater emphasis will be placed on the modernisation of looms and provision of technological and other inputs for improving productivity of hand looms and the quality and finish of handloom products;

(iii) Special efforts would be made to ensure adequate availability of yarn and other raw materials to the handloom sector. The infrastructure for procurement and supply of such inputs at reasonable prices to the handloom weavers shall be strenghtened through a operations of the National Handloom Development Corporation and the State level handloom agencies;

(iv) The production of mixed and blended'fabrics on handlooms shall be encouraged with a view to improve the wages and earnings of the weavers;

(v) Protection to handlooms will be provided reserving articles for their exclusive production in the handloom sector under the "Handloom (Reservation of Articles for Production) Act, 1985". The provisions of this Act shall be strictly enforced and the machinery for doing so shall be suitably strengthened;

(vi) To improve the competitiveness of the handlooms steps would be taken to remove, as far as possible, the cost handicap of the handlooms vis-a-vis the powerlooms by suitable fiscal measures;

(vii) To improve the marketing of handloom products, infrastructure of marketing complexes, training of marketing personnel and intensive publicity shall be organised. Steps would be taken to upgrade the technical, managerial and administrative skills of personnel employed in the handloom sector;

(viii) To strengthen the data base for the handloom sector for better planning and execution of handlooms development programmes, a census of handlooms shall be undertaken. The machinery for implementation, supervision and evaluation of handloom programmes shall be strengthened.

15. In order to improve the working conditions of the handloom weavers and to provide direct benefit to them, the following schemes, amongst others, would be introduced:

(i) A Contributory Thrift-Fund scheme to provide assistance to the handloom weavers during times of need;

(ii) A Workshed-cum-Housing scheme to provide a better place for work and living to the handloom weavers.

16. The responsibility for the entire production of controlled cloth shall be transferred to the handloom sector by the end of the Seventh Five Year Plan. The quantum of controlled cloth and janta cloth which was fixed at 650 million metres shall be suitably increased in order to provide a larger quantum of cloth at affordable prices to the poorer sections of the population. Measures will also be taken to improve the quality of cloth and to ensure that it reaches the target group. The public distribution for controlled cloth would be strengthened and streamlined.

17. All encouragement would be given to the expansion of the khadi programme in view of its large employment and income generating potential in the rural areas, specially among women. Steps would be taken to improve the production process, upgrade the skills of workers, raise productivity, diversify the product range and strengthen the marketing arrangements under the khadi programme.

18.1. The incidence of growing sickness in the textile industry, particularly in the organised mill sector, is a matter of great concern. The reasons for sickness are manifold and complex which include financial difficulties, managerial incompetence and negligence, obsolete plant and machinery, inadequate maintenance, incorrect product-mix, poor marketing, excess labour and poor industrial relations. While steps necessary to improve the health of the industry as a whole and to prevent sickness are indicated in this Statement, unit specific problems would have to be tackled on a case to case basis.

18.2. The measures needed for the revival of a sick unit have to be based on a detailed and objective study of the causes that led to sickness and identification of the steps necessary to revive the sick unit. A distinction shall have to be made between units which are potentially viable and units which are not.

18.3. In the case of potentially viable units a rehabilitation package might, inter alia, comprise of provision of additional balancing equipment, replacement of, existing machinery, change of product-mix, better marketing strategy, rationalisation of labour including improvement of work-norms, strengthening of management and organisation and adjustment of capacity in the different stages of manufacturing. In such cases, suitable financial package would need to be worked out. A nodal agency would be designated to evolve and manage this package. The financial and technical performance of such units shall be closely monitored.

18.4. In some cases, the units, although potentially viable, may have been led to sickness by inept management or mismanagement. In such cases, the existing management may have to be changed. Change of management will be essential in cases where restructuring of capital, and liabilities is contemplated.

18.5. The measures enunciated in this policy would enable some of the units to come out of their present difficulty. However, where a unit has no expectation of becoming viable in a reasonable period of time, there may be no alternative but to allow the unit to close provided the interests of the workers are protected. Takeover by the Government or nationalisation of such sick unit does not provide solution to the problems of sickness and the Government would not, as a rule, intervene in such cases.

18.6. In the process of revival of sick units and in the event of closure or liquidation, the interest of labour shall be fully protected. All possible avenues must be tried before retrenchment to minimise the social costs of transition implicit in the restructuring of the textile industry. Rationalisation of labour and revision of work-norms would need to be negotiated with labour to arrive at a satisfactory solution. The funds needed for payment of retrenchment benefit to labour shall be part of rehabilitation package and loans needed for such compensation shall be provided on concessional terms. Displaced workers would be given priority in securing employment in other units under the same management or other industrial units in the same area. Concessional finance would be made available for providing opportunities of self-employment. Workers shall also be encouraged to form cooperatives to run part or whole of the units. Schemes shall be formulated for training and retraining of labour to facilitate redeployment.

18.7. It is of utmost importance that the interest of the workers who might be displaced by permanent closure of units is safeguarded. For this purpose, schemes shall be formulated to provide relief for an interim period in addition to the statutory benefits. A Rehabilitation Fund for the workers of the textile industry would be created to provide relief to such workers for a limited period. Such a Fund shall, inter alia, be financed by a suitable cess on the textile industry.

18.8. It is necessary to monitor closely the performance of textile units to detect any sign of incipient sickness so that timely corrective measures can be taken. For this purpose, the monitoring mechanism at various levels shall be strengthened.

19.1. One of the main reasons for the present difficulties of the industry is inadequate modernisation and renovation of old and obsolete plant and machinery. Despite encouragement and incentives by the Government, the industry has only modernised to a limited extent. Government policies would aim to accelerate the pace of modernisation in the industry.

19.2. There has been very little modernisation in the ginning area, which has adversely affected the quality of cotton and hence the end-product of the industry. Expeditious replacement and modernisation of existing gins would receive priority. Concessional finance shall be made available for this purpose.

19.3. Modernisation in the spinning, weaving and processing sectors shall be undertaken on the basis of carefully identified needs of each unit as to installation of balancing equipment renovation of existing machinery, replacement and technology upgradation.

19.4. For the purpose of modernisation, adequate funds would continue to be provided with adequate measure under the soft loan scheme of the IDBI. In order to enable the industry to generate internal sources for modernisation, a Textile Modernisation Fund shall be created.

19.5. A national level Standing Advisory Committee on modernisation of the textile industry shall be set up, which would include representatives of management and labour as also suitable technical experts and representatives of financial institutions. This Committee shall identify on continuous basis the needs of modernisation and the type of modernisation that the industry should adopt.

19.6. It will be ensured that in the process of implementation of modernisation programme in the interests of workers are adequately protected.

19.7. The indigenous textile machinery manufacturing industry shall be given encouragement to reduce costs, upgrade technology and improve the quality of machinery. However, liberal import of such textile machinery, which is not manufactured indigenously, shall be permitted at or near the international prices.

19.8. For expeditious modernisation of the handlooms, research for evolution of improved types of handlooms, and adequate arrangements for ensuring swift and smooth transfer of technology from the research institutions to the handloom weavers will be given priority.

19.9. More powerloom service centres shall be established to enable the powerloom weavers to improve their skills in regard to maintenance of equipment, design development and quality of weaving.

19.10. The Textile Research Associations would be actively involved with the process of modemisation and its monitoring and their role expanded, so that they may also cater to the need of the handlooms and powerlooms.

20. The National Textile Corporation contributes significantly to the total production of yarn and fabrics in the organised sector. A number of mills under the NTC have been able to eliminate cash losses through a programme of rehabilitation. Greater effort is needed to implement programmes of selective modernisation so that as many units as possible become profitable. The continued operation of units, which are incapable of becoming viable would mean a continued drag on scarçe resources and such units or parts there of may have to be closed down to prevent any further losses. In such cases, the interest of the workers would be adequately protected. With the implementation of a programme of modernisation of equipment, strengthening and improvement *of* management, raising productivity of labour and improvement of work-culture, it is expected that NTC would provide a stabilising influence and healthy competition in the textile industry.

21. Exports from the textile sector contribute a significant portion *to* the total foreign exchange earnings derived from exports. There are however, certain constraints, both internal and external, which have meant that the full potential *of* textile exports has not yet been realised. In the international context, the Government shall

strive to bring about a liberalisation of world trade in textiles which would alleviate the external constraints on our exports. In the domestic sphere, all necessary steps would be taken to exploit our comparative advantage in this sector and to make our exports of textiles more competitive in the world market in terms of both quality and prices. For this purpose, the framework of policy would ensure that inputs for export production including capital goods. are made available at or near world prices. At the same time, it would be necessary to intensify efforts in the area of product and market development, reorient marketing strategy and create capabilities for fashion and design development. Exports of products from the handloom sector, including silk products, have considerable potential in the world market. All encouragement would be given to assist in the realisation of this potential. In so far as export production is an integral part of the total production base in the industry, the measures for restricting and modernisation of the textile industry, outlined in this Statement, shall provide the necessary impetus to exports.

22. The Government would continue to lay emphasis on the development of sericulture on account of its employment potential in the rural areas, high income generating capacity and ability to earn valuable foreign exchange through exports. Encouragement and support will continue to be given to the Central Silk Board and the State Governments for rapid development of this industry in all parts of the country. Greater attention will be given to schemes relating to production of quality seeds, plantation of improved varieties and expan- sion of sericulture activities over larger areas and achieving a higher yield per hectare. The existing extension and training services for educating the farmers in the improved techniques of silkworm rearing and control of diseases would be strengthened. Efforts shall be made for the development of technology in reeling, weaving and processing for improving the quality of the silk fabrics.

23. Government, would continue to promote the growth of the woollen sector in order to ensure adequate availability of woollens and blankets at reasonable prices to economically weaker sections, particuiarly those living in the hill regions of the country. Programmes would be undertaken to augment the indigenous raw wool production in terms of both quantity and quality. Since the indigenous raw wool production is not enough to meet the requirements of the industry,

liberal policy regarding imports of quality wool as well as shoddy would be continued. Research and development programmes will be promoted so that cheaper and better quality woollen products are developed for the domestic as well as export markets.

24. The knitting and apparel manufacturing sectors contribute significantly to employment generation and export earnings besides meeting the domestic demand for clothing. The Government shall pursue policies for strengthening, modernising and developing these sectors.

25. The existing marketing and distribution system of the industry would be reviewed to introduce changes, wherever necessary, in order to evolve a more efficient system which would reduce costs and margins and provide both consumer satisfaction and consumer protection. The institutional mechanism for market research would be strenghened.

26. The textile industry has been subjected to a number of controls and regulations, many of which have become irrelevant or unnecessary with the passage of time. Such controls would be reviewed for elimination, phasing out or modification, as the case may be.

27. Government hopes that the policy framework outlined above would facilitate the necessary restructuring of the textile industry in India, would equip it to make an increasingly significant contribution to output, employment and exports in the country and would satisfy the clothing needs of all sections of the population.

Ministry of Law and Justice
(Legislative Department)
New Delhi the 14th' August, 1986/Sravana 23, 1908 *(Saka)*

The following Act of Parliament received the assent of the President on the 14th August, 1986, and is hereby published for general information:-

THE RESEARCH AND DEVELOPMENT CESS ACT, 1986
No. 32 OF 1986

[*14th August,* 1986]

An Act to provide for the levy and collection of a cess on all payments made for the import of technology for the purposes of encouraging the commercial application of indigenously developed technology and for adapting imported technology to wider domestic application and for matters connected therewith or incidental thereto.

BE it enacted by Parliament in the Thirty-seventh Year of the Republic of India as follows:-

1. (1) This Act may be called the Research and Development Cess Act. 1986.

Short title, extent and commencement.

(2) It extends to the whole of India except the State of Jammu and Kashmir.

(3) It shall come into force on such date as the Central Government may, by notification in the Official Gazette, appoint.

Definitions

2. In this Act, unless the context otherwise requires,-

(a) "cess" means the cess levied under section 3;

18 of 1964

(b) "Development Bank" means the Industrial Development Bank of India established under section 3 of the Industrial Development Bank of India Act, 1964;

(c) "Fund" means the Venture, Capital Fund formed under section 5;

(d) "import", in relation to any technology, means the bringing into India of such technology from a place outside India;

18 of 1964.

(e) "industrial concern" has the meaning assigned to it in clause (c) of section 2 of the Indnstrial Development Bank of India Act, 1964, and includes- any other person in whose favour a foreign collaboration involving, the import of technology is approved by the Central Government;

(f) "prescribed" means prescribed by rules made under, this
Act;

(g) "specified agency" means-

2 of 1984.

(i) the Reserve Bank of India constituted Under the Reserve Bank ot India Act, 1934; or

(ii) the State Bank of India constituted under

23 of 1955. the State Bank of India Act, 1955; or

(iii) such other bank or institution as may be specified in this behalf by, the Central Government;

(h) "technology" means, any special or, technical knowledge or any special service required for any purpose whatsoever by an industrial concern under any foreign collaboration, and includes designs, drawings, publications and technical personnel.

Levy and collection of cess on payments made towards import of technology.

3. (1) There shall be levied and collected, for the purposes of this Act, a cess at such rate not excluding five per cent on all payments made towards' the import of technology, as the Central government may, from time to time, specify by notification, in the Official Gazette.

(2) The cess shall be payable to the Central Government by an industrial concern which imports technology on or before making any payments towards such import and shall be paid by the industrial concern to any specified, agency.

Crediting proceeds of cees to consolidated Fund of India.

4. The proceeds of the cess levied and collected under section 3 shall proceeds first be credited to the Consolidated Fund of India and the Central Government may, if Parliament by appropriation made by law in this behalf so provides, pay to, the Development Bank, from time to time, from out of such proceeds (after deducting the cost of collection), such sums of money as it may think fit for being utilised for the purposes of the Fund.

Venture Capital Fund.

5. (1) There shall be formed for the, purposes of this Act a Fund to be called the Venture Capital Fund and such Fund shall form part of the

18 of 1964.

Development Assistance Fund established by the Development Bank under section 14 of the Industrial Development Bank of India Act, 1964, and the provisions of Chapter V of that Act shall, save as otherwise expressly provided in this Act, apply to such Fund.

(2) There shall be credited to the Fund-

(a) all amounts paid under section 4;

(b) any amount given as grants by the Central Government for the purposes of this Act;

(c) any amount given to the Fund from any other source; and

(d) any income, from investment of - the amount in the Fund.

Application of Fund

6. The Fund shall be applied by the Development Bank: to meet the expenditure "incurred in connection with the measures and facilities which, in the opinion of the Development Bank, are necessary or expedient to provide equity capital or any other form of financial assitance to industrial concerns attempting commercial applications of indigenous technology or adapting imported technology to wider domestic applications.

Power of Central Government to exempt.

7. Notwithstanding anything contained in this Act, if the Central. Government is satisfied that it is necessary or expedient so to do in the public interest, it may, by notification in the Official Gazette and subject to such conditions, if any, as may be specified therein, exempt any industrial concern from the payment of the cess payable under this Act for the import of such technology as may be specified in such notification.

power to call for information.

8. The Development Bank may require an industrial concern to furnish, for the purposes of this Act, such statistical and other information in such form and within such period as may be prescribed.

Penalty for non-payment of cess

9. (1) If any cess payable by an industrial concerns is not paid on or before making payments towards the import of technology, it shall be deemed to be in arrears and the same shall be recovered by the Development Bank in such manner as may be prescribed.

(2) The Development Bank may, after such inquiry as it deems fit, impose on the industrial

concern, which is in arrears under sub-section (1), a penalty not exceeding ten times the amount in arrears:

Provided that before imposing such penalty, such industrial concern shall be given a reasonable opportunity of being heard, and if, after such hearing, the Development Bank is satisfied that the default was for any good and sufficient reason, no penalty shall be imposed under this sub-section.

Power to make rules.

10 (1) The Central Government may, by notification in the Official Gazette, make rules for carrying out the provisions of this Act.

(2) In particular and without prejudice to the foregoing power, such rules may provide for the following matters, namely:-

(a) the form in which and the period within which the information under section 8 may be furnished;

(b) the manner in which the arrears of cess may be recovered under sub-section (1) of section: 9;

(c) any other matter which is required to be, or may be, prescribed.

(3) Every rule made under this section shall be laid, as soon as may be after it is made, before each House of Parliament, while it is in session, for a total period of thirty days which may be comprised in one session or in two or more successive sessions, and if, before the expiry of, the session immediately following the session or the successive session aforesaid, both Houses agree in making any modification in the rule: or both Houses agree that the rule should not be made, the rule shall thereafter have effect only in such modified form or be of no effect, as the case'may'-be; so, however, that any such modification Or annulment shall' be without prejudice to the validity of anything previously done under that rule.

Industrial Policy 1988

The following is the text of anouncement made by the Ministry of industry on 3 June 1988 regarding libralisation of industrial policy.

In order to accelerate the industrial growth and give a strong impetus to the industrialisation of backward areas of the country, government have decided upon a major package of delicensing and incentives. The salient features of the decision of the government are as follows.

(A) Liberalisation of the Industrial Licensing System

The industrial licensing system as been liberalised in a very substantial manner for non-MRTP/non-FERA companies. Henceforth, there will be no need for non-MRTP/non-FERA companies to obtain industrial licences under the Industries Development and Regulation) Act, except in the following cases:

(1) Projects involving an investment in fixed assets of more than Rs. 50 crores if they are located in centrally declared backward areas for more than Rs. 15 crores if they are located in non-backward areas provided, however, that the facility of delicensing will not be available to both cases if the projects is located within:

(i) 50 kms of the periphery (i.e. boundary of the urban area limits) in cities having a population of more than 25 lakhs:

(ii) 30 kms of the periphery of cities having a population of more than 15 lakhs but less than 25 lakhs;

(iii) 15 kms of the periphery of cities having a population of more than 25 lakhs but less than 15 lakhs;

(iv) the standard urban area municipal limits of other cities and towns.

(v) Projects falling in industries induded in a "special list" (the special list is attached). This list supercedes the existing Shedules IV of the notification under the Act.

(vi) Projects which require foreign exchange for imported raw materials than steel and specified and components for more thus 30% of the value of ex-factory production from the first year of commercial production.

So far as the reservation for small size or public sector is concerned, the existing policy would continue.

(B) Development of Growth Centres

For promoting industrialisation of backward areas in an effective manner, the focus would henceforth be on the development of growth centres that would act as the magnet for attracting industries to backward areas. Such growth centres would be endowed with infrastructural facilities on par with the best available in the country, particularly in respect of power, water, telecommunications and banking.

2. To begin with, atleast 100 such growth centres would be developed, throughout the country over the next about 5 years. Each growth centre would be provided with funds of the order of Rs. 25-30 crores in order to create infrastructural facilities, of a high order. In other words, an investment of the order of Rs. 2500-3000 crores is envisaged over the, next about 5 years for creating sound and efficient infrastructural facilities in selected growth centres in backward areas. The funds for this purpose will be found by the Centre, the States and the all India financial institutions acting together.

3. The growth centres will be located within a reasonable proximity of district headquarters or tehsil headquarters in backward areas at such place that have a good potential for attracting industries. A Committe of Secretaries and representatives of all India financial institutions headed by the Secretary, Planning. Commission— is being appointed to formulate the criteria and guidelines for the selection and location of the growth centres. The States will be asked to submit their proposals for location of growth in centres in accordance with those criteria/guidelines.

4. As stated above atleast 100 growth centres would be selected to begin with and developed over the next about 5 years. Thereafter, the development of growth centres, would be further expanded so that over the next 10 to 15 years most of the backward areas of the country are covered by them. The ultimate objective is to develop one growth centre in each of the 430-odd districts in the country.

5. The development of the growth centres is in addition to the existing backward areas scheme and is not in substitution of it. However, the backward areas scheme would be reviewed periodically with the progress in the establishment of the growth centres and such modifications will be made in it as are necessary.

C. Financial incentives

At present, any new industrial undertaking established in a Centrally declared backward district is eligible to income tax relief under Section 80 HH of the Income Tax Act by way of deduction of 20% of a the profits for a period of 10 years. Furthermore, under Section 80 I of the Income Tax Act, all new industrial undertakings are entitled to an income tax relief by way of deduction of 25% of the profits for period 1 of 8 years. The benefits of both these Sections are available cumulatively to industrial undertakings established in notified backward districts. The investment allowance scheme has recently been reintroduced and industrial units will be eligible to claim its benefit also. All these benefits will be available both to the industrial units established in the growth centres as well as those located in other Centrally declared backward areas.

D. Monetary incentives

In order to provide greater assistance the norms for working capital funds required, by industrial units established in backward areas would be reviewed and they will be to accorded a more liberal treatment. The Committee under Planning Secretary would also look into this matter and make its recommendations.

The government hope these measures will give a boost, to the investment climate and industrialisation of backward areas in the country.

Industrial Licensing is Compulsory

Coal; Textiles: units operated by power: (a) All weaving units. (b) All spinning units with investment in fixed assets of more than Rs.15 crores; Milk foods and malted foods; Vegetable oils including solvent extracted oils and vanaspati; Leather, Matches; Distillation and brewing of alcoholic drinks; Hot rolling of semis, bars, wire rods and, structural sections of steel; Tractors and self-propelled combine harvestors: Motor cars, Buses, trucks, Jeeps. Vans, Scooters, Motor cycles and all other types of automobiles: Slitting/confectioning of photosensitized material from Jumbo rolls; Asbestos and Asbestos based products. Plywood, decorative veneers, particle board, medium density fibre board and block board; Sugar, All types of steel manufactured through induction and electric are furnaces; Iron and

Steel pipes and tubes, and stainless steel tubes; Wires of mild steel, special steel and alloy steel coated and uncoated; Cold and hot rolled strips, sheets and plates of all categories steel including box strappings; Non-ferrous semis, alloys, flat products and extrusions; Cold rolled formed sections; Ferro alloys; (a) Telecommunication Equipment; (b) Subscriber (End User) Communication Terminal Equipment, (c) Wireless equipment: All equipment; Computer peripherals excluding key boards and monitors; Micro-processor based industrial control instrumentation system; Electronic aerospace and defence equipment: All types; Industrial explosives, including detonating fuse, safety fuse, gun powder and nitrocellulose;

Chemicals (other than fertilisers)

Sodium/Potassium Chlorate; Calcium Carbonate, Calcium Carbide, Elemental Phosphorous, BHC Technical, m-amino phenol, m-Dinitro benzene, Nitro benzenes, Nitro chloro benzenes, 'Nitro' toluenes, Alcohol based chemicals : lamely Acetaldehyde, Acetic Acid, cetic Anhydride, Ethyl Atetate and Diethyl either, Formaldehyde. Nylon chips/Nylon moulding powder, Polyester chips/ polyester moulding powder, Industrial alcohol, Sodium/Potassium Cyanide,) Pesticides/Insecticides formulations. based on technical material obtained from sources other than own manufacture, Carbaryl, Quinalphos, Dimethoate, Aluminium Phosphide, Isoproturon, Phorate, Monocrotophes, Carbondazin, Fenitrophion, 6-APA.

3.11 Challenges are Apportunities

Our scientists have made considerable achievements these years. They have put India in a strong, self-reliant position not just in agriculture, but also in certain strategic and sensitive areas, where it was difficult for us to import technology, where there has been a real challenge, where the chips are down, our scientists have risen to the occasion and have shown the world that they are second to none when it comes to capability, competence and achievements.

Today the challenge that our scientists and technologists face is greater than the challenge that our scientists faced a couple of thousands of years ago. The challenge now is not just to catch up with to equal what is going on in the rest of the world, but the challenge is to surpass and once more give the lead that we used to some thousands of years ago. Our scientists must concentrate on what is meaningful for a country like India.

And in today's circumstances that means in the rural areas, the agricultural sector and the various sectors that support our agriculture. We have seen by experience, that, where we have set out a particular task or challenge, our scientists and technocrats have responded and delivered. Perhaps it was seeing a goal in front of them...[1] Rajiv Gandhi said -

> *Our scientists have many achievements behind them. They have made us self-reliant in very basic areas. Whether it is in food, whether it is in certain strategic areas of defence, in space, in nuclear sciences, they have shown that, where there is a challenge, they are upto that challenge and they have the capacity to lift India up when they are given that chance and when they are given full backing.*
>
> *We have shown that when India accepts a challenge, when our scientists accept a challenge, when our technologists accept a challenge, they need that challenge and they deliver the goods. Today, we must give them the backing that they need to achieve similar results in many other fields.*
>
> *Where science and technology is concerned, we must keep in mind that nothing but the best will do for the country; and we must work towards that end. With everybody's support, I believe we will be able to do it*[2].

Our science will flourish to the extent it is self-confident and open-minded, keeps abreast of what is happening in the rest of the world, recognizes excellence and exchanges ideas and concepts, technologies and techniques. The pyramid, to be stable, must have a sound and broad base. The talent at the top must be supported by thousands below.[3]

Unfortunately or fortunately, the speed at which development is taking place all over the world is very very high. If we are to catch up with the most advanced countries, we must go faster than they are going today. Otherwise there is no catching up. We cannot go faster if we do not think ahead of them. ... And then let us work on that; let us be in the frontline. ... We will not be the best unless we are thinking well beyond what anybody else is thinking about. ... Innovation is the one word, which will represent what you must try and do. By merely trying to see what others have done, we are not going to benefit.[4]

> *Our national goal must be self-reliance. We have shown, our scientists have shown over the years, that India can become self-reliant in critical areas.*
>
> *We have to look at things in terms of what we want to make of India. ... We have been having inward looking policies in development areas. We have to look at where we want to take the country, what are the challenges that the country will be facing, other challenges – and what we need to do to strengthen ourselves to face these challenges.*[5]
>
> *If in the current shift in global relationships, we are not able to ensure for India her rightful place, we may perhaps miss a good opportunity. We may not get an opportunity for decades to come to correct this situation. We should not miss this opportunity.*

Rajiv Gandhi said that ... the colossal problems that we face at the dawn of independence – the problem of hunger, disease and ignorance. It is to these problems that the sensitive mind and the spirit of Jawaharlal Nehru sought solutions. And the solutions that he sought were in the domain of science and technology. Science has expanded man's power to control his destiny.[6]

> *... From the moment of our freedom, we linked science with development. For us, science was the liberation, not the destroyer. For us, science was the enhancement of life, not its extinction. Therefore, in our vision, science was an ally of peace.*

Rajiv Gandhi said the above at the Valedictory Session of the International Symposium on science, Technology and Development, on 25 March 1987. "As scientists, you have the power to show us the way. You are not only men and women of science, you are citizens of the human race endowed with unique ability. You are able to understand the physical world better than others. You have the means to transform it. You owe it to humankind that this special gift is used in the service of peace.

After 40 years of freedom, the time has now come for us to take stock and see what we need to do to quicken the pace of our progress. We need to do this across the board. We must, therefore, do this in the context of science and technology as well. ... I would urge you to consider what the scientific community and the authority must do in the coming years, to meet the challenge. ..."[7] Keeping the practical aspects of the world situation in mind, Rajiv Gandhi attempted a definite approach to the question of peace. Removal of poverty and rapid growth of economy are the top priorities of the modern urban India.

It was November 1989. The Congress party could not win the election with majority, and was voted out of power. Rajiv Gandhi sent in his resignation to the President of India, on 29 November 1989. In his broadcast to the nation, on that evening, he said –

> *"Elections are won and lost. We shall not falter in our resolve to do our duty by India ... With all my strength, I shall continue to serve the people of India".*

He was then elected Leader of the Congress Legislature Parliamentary Party and Leader of the Opposition in the Parliament.

References

1. Rajiv Gandhi — 73rd Session, Indian Science Congress Association, New Delhi, 8 January 1986.
2. — Speech in the Lok Sabha, 10 April 1986.
3. — 74th Session, Indian Science Congress Association, Bangalore, 3 January 1987.
4. — Conference, Directors of National Laboratories of CSIR, New Delhi, 28 May 1986.
5. — Presenting the Shanti Swarup Bhatnagar Award for Science and Technology, New Delhi, 17 October 1988.
6. — Valedictory address, International Symposium on Science, Technology and Development, New Delhi, 25 March 1987.
7. — Inaugural Address, 75th Session, Indian Science Congress Association, Pune, 7 January 1988.

4

The Un-finished Agenda of Rajiv Gandhi A Man of Vision Lives Forever

...... Education is more than just reading the sciences and reading biotechnology or specializing in particular spheres. I think, the primary goal of our education has to be the development of the human being to be a better human being. All our aims, whether they are technological or scientific, must be towards the same end. When we are able to achieve and move towards this target, we shall really see a betterment coming about in India......

—Rajiv Gandhi

It was election time in April – May, 1991,· Rajiv Gandhi, campaigned on the strength of his past performance of his government record of 5 years and its performance for the future. He won the election and the Congress Legislative also came into power again. But India and the entire world was shocked at the tragic and dastardly assassination of Rajiv Gandhi. A very young and maturing politician, who had raised world expectations through his sincerity of purpose, was murdered in a ghastly act, disrupting the democratic process of elections to the (Parliament) Lok Sabha on 21 May 1991.

Every great man leaves behind him certain tasks to be completed after him. Rajiv Gandhi had the vision to build a new India of 21st century. He told Barbara Crosette[1] of the New York Times, who was travelling with him during the election tour, a few minutes before his sudden demise that -

> *"But we have to do so much more,"*
>
> *"We have to make the system much more efficient."*
>
> *Rajiv Gandhi mused about some of the plans he had for the next administration he hoped to form after the elections. Commenting on the popular criticism of the government, for instance – on controlled television services in India, he talked about opening up broadcasting to private corporations, but under "some sort" of government oversight. "We will not allow it to end up as regional chauvinisms," he said. Besides discussing developmental issues such as Indo—Pak relations, separatism in Indian States, Controversies over religion, etc.*
>
> *He talked about education, one of his favourite subjects. He said he wanted to free the highly politicised universities from too much control and let them find their own level. "Some will be good, and some will be bad," he said. "Now they are all awful." He argued that family planning was "very much a non-starter" in India. "**We need four things,**" he said. "We need education for the woman, the girl child. We need good jobs for everybody. We need child and maternal health care. And, we need overall economic growth. The government must act so that the result is family planning, which would follow these things."*

He talked about the prosperity; he gave us some and would have given more, had he lived longer. He had endless dreams.... dreams for the young, dreams for the nation.

I have a lot of unfinished things to do – so said Rajiv Gandhi even during as a leader of the opposition in Parliament, in 1989-91. He was a restless soul, waiting for the right opportunity to launch new programmes towards techno-economic development as well as the emergence of a new India.

Shri P Chidambram said that... "a few months ago, Rajiv Gandhi set up a group of eminent persons to advise him on economic and national security matters. He was preparing for a second innings and was determined to score the century that he had missed in his first innings. The high point in recent week was the Congress election manifesto. His first term as Prime Minister was marked by a vision largely technocratic and relying heavily on science and technology. In the 15 months that he took to prepare himself for the next term, this vision had been greatly tampered and re-inforced by a newfound practical vision. Much of this is reflected in the last chapter of the Congress manifesto, which contains a time bound programme. We worked on this together for three full days, I told him that only if he had the will to implement these promises, should we put them into the manifesto. He assured me that he was determined to implement them. I am sure, he would have done so and he would have ushered in a veritable revolution in the first 100 days in office. The manifesto and the time – bound programme are the legacy that Rajiv has left for the party and the nation".[2]

Rajiv Gandhi was so confident of his coming back to the power, in 1991, that he was already working on a blue print for science and technology and had a grandiose scheme for the restructuring of scientific establishments, to free them from the stranglehold of bureaucracy. He was interested in getting things done fast, and did not believe in adding new institutions for science. He was for consolidating the strength of science and technology in India, said Prof CNR Rao. President, Jawahar Lal Nehru Centre for Advanced Scientific Research, Bangalore.

Proposed New Agricultural Package

Agriculture contributes the major part in our economy. Eighty percent of the Indian population depend on agriculture. The status of our farmers is abysmal. The rot in India's agriculture is all pervasive: Poor credit facilities, skewed support prices, unscrupulous middlemen and an indifferent government contribute to a farmer's woes. Rajiv Gandhi outlined his priority task for his next term, that would have heralded a bright new era for the whole farming community. While presenting a new Agricultural Package, in the Lok Sabha (Parliament) on 12 October 1989, the then Prime Minister Rajiv Gandhi drew attention to his proposed action plan (say, the unfinished agenda).[3] To quote him:

> *"We are determined to accord the highest priority to agriculture in the Eighth Five-Year Plan, 1990-95. Agricultural growth must be accelerated. Agricultural income and employment must grow faster than they have in the past. Our kisans (farmers) are concerned at the process of determining support prices for farm produce. We shall ensure that two major modifications are introduced in the method of computing the cost of production while fixing support prices for agricultural produce.* ***First****, we shall determine the wage costs on the basis of the statutory minimum wage for agricultural labour notified by the State or the actual wages paid, whichever is higher.* ***Second,*** *we shall include in the cost of production, the labour input of the kisan at a higher wage reflecting the managerial and entrepreneurial role of the kisan."*
>
> *"In order to enable kisans to rationally determine their cropping pattern, support prices are being notified by the Government in advance of the sowing. However, this system leaves out of account the increases in costs taking place between the point of announcement and the point of harvesting. To remedy this, we are instructing the CACP (Commission for Agricultural Costs and Prices) to work out suitable escalation formula.*
>
> *"These rates will also apply to those farmers who have already sold the produce in the current kharif*

marketing season. The farming community has also been concerned at the terms of trade for the farm sector in relation to other sectors. The adverse movement of the terms of trade has been rectified to some extent in the Sixth and Seventh Plans. ***In the Eighth Five Year Plan, we shall ensure favourable terms of trade for the farming sector.***

"Many farmers are not able to obtain the advantage of minimum support prices because procurement centers are sometimes at a considerable distance from their farms and villages. We intend to increase the number of procurement centers so that, eventually, every kisan will have access to a procurement center within 10 Kms of his village. The rural roads network will also be strengthened in a phased manner. Kisans, particularly those engaged in the farming of perishable farm commodities, are often denied a fare share of the value of their produce because of the very perishability of their produce. The only answer lies in expanding rural godowns and cold - or cooled – storage facilities in rural areas.

"There is scope for substantially improving credit facilities for the farm community. ***We propose four steps in this regard:***

"First*, we must rectify the problem of credit not being available to members of cooperatives to which they belong, having become ineligible for NABARD refinance. We have decided to open, with effect from the ensuing rabi season, a special line of credit of Rs. 100 crore through cooperative and commercial banks which will be earmarked exclusively for Scheduled Caste and Scheduled Tribe farmers.*

"Second, *scales of finance for short-term production credit will be revised annually so that the credit made* *available to the farmer fully meets the recommended doses of input at current prices to meet his cultivation requirements.*

*"**Third,** a special credit regime is being instituted for kisans in rain fed farming areas covered by watershed development programmes. The new regime will operate on the basis of ensuring the availability of credit through a three – to - five year cycle so as to even out the inherent risk involved in good and bad monsoon years appearing in a cycle in such areas. The special credit regime will take into account problem of overdues which arise within a cyclical period to ensure an adequate flow of credit in support of viable crop production and other allied activities. This regime will be reinforced by a major programme of watershed development in rain fed farming areas.*

*"**The fourth step** we propose is essentially a procedural one but which kisans will immediately recognize as being of utmost importance to their requirements. Passbooks and Agriculture Credit Cards will be extended to kisans so as to enable the easy withdrawal of production loans from cooperative and commercial banks.*

"The National Agricultural Credit Relief Fund will devise a comprehensive relief policy based on the special characteristics of production and the severity of damage in different agro-climate zones. Through the rescheduling of loans and waivers of interest and principal in defined circumstances, the credit needs of farmers in different zones will be kept in view. While we have invested astronomical sums of money in land improvement and irrigation, our management of land and water resources has been so poor as to render the benefits secured far below the optimum achievable. We propose to take a number of steps to improve the management of our land and water resources.

"During the next five years**, irrigation waters will be made available on an assured basis to an additional one crore hectares of land in the command areas of canal projects. The authorities concerned will be held responsible for reaching water to farmers in assured quantities and at the right time. Also, ten lakh tube-wells and dug-wells are to be constructed every year. And five lakh hectares will be covered annually for the programme of desilting and maintenance of village tanks, beels, bunds and ponds. **Second,** the productivity of un-irrigated land is to be enhanced through effective watershed development and in situ moisture conservation. This programme will extend to 50 lakh hectares during the next five years." **Third,** 25 lakh hectares of usar and barani land will be reclaimed at the rate of five lakh hectares a year. **We need not wait for the commencement of the Eighth Plan to take up these projects. A beginning should be made this year itself.

"Plasticulture holds vast potential for increasing agricultural productivity. The uses of plastic are many, especially in irrigation, storage and packaging. Existing plasticulture schemes will be substantially expanded. It is proposed to extend incentives for the installation of sprinkler or drip irrigation systems to all farmers. During the next five years, one lakh additional sprinkler systems and one lakh drip irrigation systems will be installed to optimize the use of scarce water resources.

"Good seeds are the basic foundation of higher agricultural productivity. The New Seed Policy is under implementation and the buffer stocks being built will ensure that kisans have access to high quality seeds and planting material at reasonable prices. We are particularly concerned about small, marginal and SC / ST farmers. With effect from rabi 1989 – 90, mini kits for the supply of improved seeds will be ensured, under

the existing centrally – sponsored schemes to 20 lakh such farmers.

"Agricultural research is simply not getting the attention or priority it needs. We are reconstituting the Indian Council of Agricultural Research and I shall take over as its president". **We have two major objectives in mind: First,** we propose to generate appropriate technologies for each sub – zone of the 15 agro – climatic zones so as to be able to modernise our agriculture in each of the zones. **Second,** a special time – bound programme in research and development of hybrids is being taken up to cover rice, maize, jowar, bajra, arhar, cotton and oilseeds. Results will be demanded within five years and the implementation of the research programme will be monitored at the highest level. To promote the manufacture of agricultural machinery and implements of improved design, particularly those using new and more efficient materials, **a Special fund** is being established to extend credit for the manufacture, fabrication and marketing of such machinery and implements, as also for the leasing or custom hiring of such machinery and implements, plant protection equipment and sprinklers.

"For adding value to primary produce, as also expanding employment opportunities in rural areas, it is necessary to encourage agro-based industries, particularly food processing. A special extension and infrastructure package is being put in place for the development and processing of fruits and vegetables in suitable areas. Also, incentives are being given to industrial units to enter into contracts with small producers individually or through cooperatives. For the diversification of rural economic activity, Fish Farmers Development Agencies are being established in all coastal districts to encourage pisciculture and aquaculture. Special attention will be given to poultry *development and sheep farming, including reduced costs of feed, market support for the stabilization of egg prices, incentives to establish processing complexes in rural areas linked to small farms, and support to the export of processed products.*

"Agriculture has the potential of becoming a major export sector. Our kisans will benefit from linking agricultural production to lucrative export markets. In order to realize this potential, we propose to extend incentives to expand the production base of exportable commodities as also the range of non-traditional agricultural exports.

"Major institutional reforms are required to support this package. We have two important programmes in hand in this regard. ***First,*** *we are initiating a programme to update and computerize land records so that farmers can obtain documentation on demand.* ***Second,*** *we propose to reform, revamp and rejuvenate the cooperative movement, which, in many parts of the country, and in many ways, has failed to play the central role envisaged for the cooperative movement in our strategy of socio-economic transformation.* ***This is a priority task for our next term in office****. The interests of agriculture are the interests of the nation. There is no dichotomy between agricultural development and national development. The former is the foundation of the latter. We are confident that the agricultural package, I am now placing before the House, will herald a bright new era for our kisans, khet-mazdoors and for the whole farming community."*

He certainly required another term to put his new found ideas together and launch his policies into action for the agricultural development leading to national economic development. Fate has taken him away when he was almost back in power. He was about to get a second chance. Alas, that was not to be. He was a catalyst of progress. Unfortunately, he died in the prime of his youth and did not live long to see the fulfillment of his dreams. Had he lived longer, he would have certainly contributed more to the techno-economic development of India and the world.

A Big Loss to the Science in India:

A condolence meeting was organized by the leading scientists and technologists of India, on 4 June 1991, at the India International Center, New Delhi, to pay homage to Rajiv Gandhi. All the speakers who had close interaction with the assassinated leader in their official capacities paid glowing tributes to the interest taken by him, in matters relating to the development of science and technology. The scientific community felt that:

> *We hoped that he will lead us into the 21st century...raise the status of India in the comity of nations...at a time when the old is collapsing and the new is struggling to be born, what India needed was a leader like Rajiv Gandhi...The nation has lost a unique leader.*

Prof. C. N. R. Rao, an eminent scientist revealed the instant reaction of Rajiv Gandhi when it was suggested to him that India should take up the lead in Super-conductivity research, as a result of which an apex body was set up for coordinating the R & D at various institutes in the country. Further, Rajiv Gandhi gave full support to the recommendations of the Science Advisory Council to the Prime Minister (SAC-P) relating to the need to set up an apex body, National Science and Technology Council for coordinating the programmes and activities related to science and technology in the socio-economic sectors.

Dr. V. S. Arunachalam, the then Scientific Advisor to Raksha Mantri (Defence Minister), said Rajiv Gandhi had interest in promoting the long range missile programme of the Defence forces, and foresaw the need for precision and accuracy and importance of missile based defence technology which had now been demonstrated in the Gulf war. Mr. Sam Pitroda, Chairman, Telecom Commission, gave a heart-warming account of Rajiv Gandhi's role in the national telecom development and role in bringing computers within common man's life. He said that, "*I saw Rajiv Gandhi more as a concept. He had a modern mind, a vision for India*".

Shri V. Krishnamurthy recalled the "*deep understanding*" of Rajiv Gandhi in regard to the role of technology in industry and the place of modern management techniques. He revealed several anecdotes where Rajiv Gandhi discussed at length the problems of application of technology in the public sector industries. *"To us, the technocrats, Mr. Gandhi was the answer"*, former SAIL chairman said.

Dr. P.K. Iyengar claimed that the "*country has benefited*" from the perception of the three Prime Ministers – Jawaharlal Nehru, Indira Gandhi and Rajiv Gandhi. Our technologies have been more cost effective than those of many other advanced nations", said former Chairman, Atomic Energy Commission. These eminent scientists of India, recalled Rajiv Gandhi's "*child like inquisitive and open mind"* and attention to details.

Prof. M.G. K. Menon, an eminent scientist said that – *Rajiv Gandhi was a young man in a hurry.* He wanted to deal with the total problem and not just a part of it. He himself took great interest in several projects. Prof. Menon drew attention to the several technology missions that were launched during Mr. Gandhi's tenure: these missions he said, expressed the former Prime Minister's ambition to do something really big for the benefit of the people using science and technology.

Prof Yash Pal, former Chairman, University Grants Commission, New Delhi, said that in these years of fiscal prominence, globalisation, restructuring and market mechanism, the emphasis on scientific and technological achievement, or educational excellence, had weakened somewhat. Consistency would demand just the opposite. Many scientists have talked of the special rapport they had with Rajiv Gandhi. The exuberant in this constituency will miss his sense of hurry and his impatience, he said.

Prof. Manmohan Singh, Chairman, UGC, expressed, "the deepest sorrow at the sad and most untimely death of Rajiv Gandhi". In a statement, he said that the "barbaric and cowardly act deserves universal condemnation". He further said – As P.M. of India, Rajiv Gandhi worked to build a modern technologically advanced, cohesive and humane polity and society in India. His life and work will continue to inspire our people to wage a relentless war against poverty, ignorance, diseases and against communal and cast hatred and violence.

A **Joint Statement** was passed at the end of the condolence meeting, which stated:

> ***...Rajiv Gandhi was the prime mover of the vitally important technology missions in India.***
>
> ***...He wanted science and technology to help in the alleviation of poverty and eradication of mediocrity in all walks of life and wanted the scientific attitude to percolate down to all citizens.***
>
> ***...He felt science and technology had not only to contribute to the solutions of the problems related to the basic needs of the common man, but also make India competitive in basic research in science, technology (blue sky research) and industry.***
>
> ***... He was not only genuinely interested in science and technology, but was personally involved in the various programmes and projects.***
>
> ***...He personally contributed to the development of various areas including atomic energy, space, ocean development, defence, science, telecommunication, industrial research and electronics.***

> ***We will badly miss Mr. Gandhi. Those of us who had the pleasure of working with him closely will never forget his compassion, his geniality and affection. His partiality towards the scientific community was unprecedented. Today, the scientific community formally salutes Mr. Rajiv Gandhi.***
>
> ***In paying tribute to this great personality, who adorned the Indian scene, the scientific community can pay its homage only by rededicating itself to the cause that he believed in, namely, of bringing all round development in India through science and technology. The scientific community earnestly hopes that this ideal of Mr. Gandhi will not be forgotten in the years to come.***
>
> ***Mr. Rajiv Gandhi represented a dynamic force. In his passing away, we have not just lost a person, but a direction for the future of science and technology in India.***

A resolution was passed unanimously to express their shock at the "devastating tragedy" caused by the assassination of Mr. Rajiv Gandhi and to convey their condolences to his widow, Mrs. Sonia Gandhi, his son Rahul and daughter Ms. Priyanka Gandhi.

Rajiv Gandhi dreamt of a new India and worked towards that dream. His untimely death at the age of 47 cut short his dream of building technologically advanced India of the 21st century. It is a great tragedy that when he could give his best to the service of mother India, the heinous conspirators snatched him from us. He gave us so much in the short span of his life. He gave us:

A dream to live up to…
A path to walk on…
A vision to fulfill...
A mission to achieve…

Rajiv Gandhi symbolized the new generation in India – bold, energetic and innovative. Our best tribute to this great soul and the light of the nation would be to learn from his life and contributions, strive to do better in our own way in our lives and work. He was conferred India's highest award - Bharat Ratna (Jewel of India) posthumously on 17 June 1991, for his selfless service to the nation. He left an indelible mark, in his brief political career, on the overall growth of India. He was the creator of the vibrant force of change. The Rajiv Gandhi Foundation, New Delhi, apart from keeping his legacy fresh and alive, is expanding its work into critical areas for the social upliftment of the people.

The fragrance of your spirit
fills the hearts
of all those whose lives you touched with your warmth.

References

1. Barbara Crosette- We have to do much more, The Times of India, 26 May 1991, New Delhi.
2. P. Chidambaram – He lived too dangerously, The Times of India, 26 May 1991, New Delhi.
3. Rajiv Gandhi – Speech in the Lok Sabha, 12 October 1989.

Notes

1. Prof. M.G.K. Menon, eminent scientist, paid his sincere tibutes to Rajiv Gandhi, through the media.
2. Prof. S.K. Joshi, the then Director-General, Council of Scientific and Industrial Research (CSIR), New Delhi, remained in the background, though the condolence meeting war organised by the CSIR, Eyebrows were raised within the scientific community about the Government funded this meeting to condole the death of Rajiv Gandhi who was then the leader of the opposition, in the ninth Lok Sabha.

5

Rajiv Gandhi on Rajiv Gandhi A Self-Assessment of his Dynamic Years

We must remember that the primary problem that we face in India is one of removing poverty and keeping in mind that the litmus test for any national activity is how it helps in removing poverty. How can modern scientific and technological knowledge be brought to bear on the task of removing poverty? The challenge has been in front of us.

—Rajiv Gandhi

"The 21st century does not mean just computers, although to an average person, technology means computers and television and fancy data communication links and satellites; advanced technology also means genetic engineering, making seeds better, making them resistant to disease, making them more productive, seeing what else the farmer needs as back up, tractors, implement, power, water, fertilizer. That too is technology. We have to give the best so that the farmer can perform his best", said Rajiv Gandhi to a group of children, assembled at his residence on 8 July 1985.

Development for Rajiv Gandhi, did not mean just producing more machines. He visualized a modern and dynamic India with a developed agriculture and industrial base, overcoming poverty and providing equity of opportunities to all. He realized that this was possible only by spreading education and bringing the benefits of science and technology to every household. He believed that the technology gap between India and the developed countries needs to be bridged. He said-

> *When I started talking of the twenty-first century, of building India for the twenty-first century, I did not have a picture of computers popping out of every village shop or every home. I was really thinking of how we were going to change mental attitutudes in the twenty-first century.*

The Vision of India

The following excerpt of his interview with John Elliot of Financial Times, London, on 4 April 1985, gives his fresh approach to the problems facing the country :

Q -Judging by the speed with which you have initiated changes, you could not have been too happy about what you watched happening before you, when you could do little or nothing about it.

R.G.: *The younger generation always feels that things are not moving fast enough and may be this will be true 20 years from now.*

Q -Turning to industry, you have relaxed a lot of industrial licenses and controls, allowed more imports in, and opened up areas for the private sector. How far do you really want to move the country away from its traditional protectionism and centralism?

R.G.: *It depends on specific areas. On strategic and core areas like energy, telecommunications, defence and transport and to some degree, we don't want to ease up too much and it should remain largely in the public sector. From our strategic point of view, we think it is necessary that it does so. In other areas we are not going to be very fussy about letting the private sector in and loosening up the controls.*

Q - How open an economy should India become?

R.G.: *When we started our development, we had a particular policy because there was a particular condition. We didn't have the capability to have a private industry. The management, the technology, the know-how were not available. So, we had to build the public sector and we had to build everything in the public sector. Now we have built up that technological manpower and we must use it.*

So, areas where we feel it is strategically important for us to have government control, which includes things like food distribution for example, it is important that the government keeps tabs because we cant be blackmailed on that.

But in other areas where we have developed a know-how, developed a technology, I think we should ease up and let people in – I am talking about Indian private sector as opposed to foreign private sector.

Q - Your policies are being criticized because, while you are cutting tariffs on many products not made here, you are building in new protection with very high tariff barriers like 200 percent on computers and components made in India. So, you are building in new higher technology protectionism.

R.G.: *You have got to give them some protection till they find their feet otherwise they will never find their feet. But we are not reintroducing protectionism at a higher point.*

Q - Do you have an economic model that you admire or follow – say Japan or Singapore?

R.G.: *We are going to develop our own model, as every country must for its own system to suit its own people.*

The challenge of piloting a nation like India, having large democracy, poor population, different religions, sects, casts and creeds etc., into the 21st century was a daunting one for the young and maturing politician - who was once reluctant to entering politics. When Rajiv Gandhi visited the United States on 13 June, 1985, an interview with Ted Koppel of ABC's 'Nightline' produced a fascinating by-play. Koppel questioned the young Prime Minister:

Forgive me; because this sounds, I suppose, like a rather indelicate question. But how does some one go from five years ago, having no role in politics, to suddenly being the Prime Minister of the world's largest democracy. A huge jump!

Rajiv's answer was quick, short, penetrating ... and even humourous. *Well, we have a fantastic thing called the democratic process.*

How would you like history to record your own legacy? — asked another British journalist from London, to the Prime Minister, Rajiv Gandhi, on 4 July 1985. As a modest and soft-spoken person, he replied,

> "......*well as having brought India, into the twenty- first century, paralleled with more advanced countries in the world, out of branding India as a developing country to the status of a developed country.* He had a vision of modern India. He further added with his usual humour that- *When India solves problems, it solves the problems of a sixth of humanity.*[1,2]

He said that with science and technology in a short period, we have transformed India, formerly a country of famines, into a country that is strong, resilient, self-sufficient. It is a story of success for the whole world to see.[3]

Later, When asked by another journalist, *to sum up his five years as Prime Minister of India, 1984-89,*"—moments he handed over the charge to the next incumbent, Rajiv Gandhi said that— "*I think India has never had the sort of development and progress and international standing that it has gained in these five years*".[4]

How will history judge Rajiv Gandhi? According to Minhaz Merchant, his success was limited, but he will be remembered for infusing a technocratic vigour, however short- lived, into the Indian politics.[5] There is no doubt Rajiv Gandhi was instrumental in fostering an atmosphere of modernity in the country. India surged ahead with him. He was a remarkable man and responsible for making what India is today.

References

1. N. Nugent – Rajiv Gandhi : Son of Dynasty, British Broadcasting Corporation, London, p. 75, 1990.
2. Eastern Eye, London 4 July 1985.
3. Kathleen Healy – Rajiv Gandhi: The Years of Power, Vikas Publishing House Pvt. Ltd, p. 29, 1989, New Delhi.
4. Rajiv Gandhi – Foundation Day Celebrations, CSIR, New Delhi, 26 September 1987.
5. Minhaz Merchant – Rajiv Gandhi : The End of Dream. Viking, New Delhi.

SCIENTIFIC ACHIEVEMENTS MADE DURING THE PRIME MINISTERSHIP OF RAJIV GANDHI (31 October 1984 – 29 November 1989)

1. Formation of an Apex Body
    - Science Advisory Council to the Prime Minister set up on 4 February 1986.
2. Computer Movement
    - Announced Computer policy for India on 19 November 1984.
3. Electronics and Telecommunication

    Established –
    - Centre for the Development of Telecommunication (C-DOT).
    - National informatics Centre (NIC), New Delhi.
    - Centre of Development of Advance Computing Application, C-DAC
4. Technology Missions

Launched for the first time, six Technology Missions in India-
- Drinking water supply.
- Oil Seeds Mission.
- Reduction in Illiteracy.
- Better Communication.
- Mass Immunization.
- Milk Production.

5. Education:
    - New Education Policy – 1986 announced in May 1986.
6. Environment Protection
    - Created a new Department of Environment (later upgraded to the Ministry of Environments and Forests).
    - Environment Protection Act – 1986 announced on 23 May 1986.
    - National Forest policy – 1988 announced on 7 December 1988.

Set up –
- Central Ganga Authority, New Delhi for the implementation of Ganga Action Plan.

- National Wasteland Development Board.

Introduction of –

- A new mechanism of assessing the Environmental impact of development work – requirement of essentiality certificate.
- Planet Protection Fund (PPF), under the aegis of the United Nations.

7. Agriculture and Rural Development
   - Presented a New Agriculture Package in Parliament on 12 October 1989.
   - New policy on Seed Development announced on 18 September 1988.
   - Krishi Vigyan Kendras established in all Districts of India.
   - National Water Policy – announced in1987.
8. Technology Innovation and Industrial Development
   - Research and Development Cess Act – 1986 announced on 14 August 1986.
   - New Industrial Policy, June 1988.
   - Statement on Textile Policy, June 1985.
   - New Drug Policy, 28 June 1988.
9. Non-Conventional Sources of Energy
   - Large scale production and promotion of Solar Cookers, Solar water-heaters, Solar photovoltaic Panels etc.
10. New Scientific Infrastructure
    - Creation of - a Ministry of Science and Technology in 1985 with DST, DBT and DSIR (1st time).
    - Department of Ocean Development, New Delhi
    - Setting up TIFAC, New Delhi
    - Indo-French Centre for the Promotion of Advanced Scientific Research, New Delhi.
    - Centre for Science and Technology for the Non-Aligned and other Developing Countries, New Delhi.
    - National Center for Medium Range Forecasting (with super computer), New Delhi.
    - National Natural Resources Management system (NRDMS), New Delhi.
    - National Super Conductivity Programme.
    - Jawahar Lal Nehru Centre for Advanced Scientific Research, Bangalore etc.

11. International Cooperation
    - Gandhi – Reagan Forum on science and Technology with USA, in 1985.
    - Integrated Long-Term Programme (ILTP) of Cooperation in Science and Technology with USSR, in 1986 etc.
12. New Concept
    - Brain drain *termed* as Brain Bank.

6

Epilogue

21st Century Sans Rajiv Gandhi

We trust the people; we have faith in the people, it is the people who must determine their own destinies and the destiny of the Nation. To the people of India, let us ensure maximum democracy and maximum devolution, let the people be empowered.

—**Rajiv Gandhi**

Science is an integral part of our culture. At least partly, we owe this to the influence on our subconscious from the brilliant scientists in our history-from Barhma gupta and Bahskaracharya to Bhabha and Raman. Their existence proves that a scientific tradition has always been alive in the Indian culture.

Pandit Jawahar Lal Nehru had a vision of India. Like his grandfather, Rajiv Gandhi too had a vision of a new and resurgent India. These were his genuine feelings and he learnt democratic values from Pandit Nehru, who said in the Discovery of India, in 1951: "The human mind appeared to have a passion for finding out some kind of unity in life, in nature and the Universe. That desire, whether it is justified or not, must fulfill some essential need of the mind. The old philosophers were seeking this; even modern scientists are compelled by this urge. All our schemes and planning our ideas of education, social and political have at their back the search for unity and harmony". Pandit Nehru further said in 1957 - *Parliamentary democracy, thus includes peaceful methods of action, peaceful acceptance of decisions taken and attempts to change them through peaceful ways again.*

Rajiv Gandhi, like Nehru, too had a great faith in democracy. On the question of economic progress, He, in his maiden speech in the Lok Sabha, on 22 January 1985, said –

> *I look forward from all friends in the opposition, whether they are in this House or other parties in the opposition who are not in the House. If both the opposition members as well as, those of the ruling party work together to achieve this aim (of economic progress) much can be done.*

Rajiv Gandhi said: What is the difference between the first half and the second half of the twentieth century? The difference is basically: the scientific knowledge, scientific input and equally important, their application at the field level, which means it is the team work between our scientists, our extension workers, and ... that had lead to this.[1]

Rajiv Gandhi as an icon of modernism, and was largely instrumental in shaping the science and its development in India of the 21st century. His task during the fag end of 20th century was a daunting one. Consequently as we enter the new millennium, it is an appropriate moment to assess his wisdom and contributions, which remains as a signpost for the present and the future.

New India

The economy in India is on a high, with a GDP growth of over 9 % as on March 2007. The manufacturing industry in finally gearing up for a long overdose revival, alongwith- automobile and component industy. The electronics industry is growing as well. The service industry, including IT, ITES, Telecom together with insurance and retail sectors are on the roll. According to Swaminathan S. Ankelesaria, "When India opened its economy in 1991, leftists warned that uncompetitive Indian companies would be killed or swallowed up by multinationals. Fifteen years later, the shoe is on the other foot: Indian companies are taking over giant multinationals.

"India has left behind the stage of being seen as a global supplier of software, generic drugs and auto components. It is now seen as a global managerial power, one that can take over MNCs across the world and improve their performance.

"The world now believes that Indians are excellent managers, better than those in several American and European countries. What used to be biggest companies in the world, General Motors and Ford, today have a credit rating far lower than that of Tata, Birla, Reliance and other Indian groups. Indian companies can raise cheap international finance to acquire American giants, but not the other way round. Hundreds of Indian companies have become MNCs with growing empires. This is only the beginning of the great Indian takeover. Indian companies should aim for the sky over the next two decades."

Mr. Shashi Tharoor of the United Nations, said -

"India's extraordinary emergence in new-age industries – software, Information Technology and Business Process Outsourcing – is the indirect result of Jawaharlal Nehru's faith in the scientific education. Nehru left India with the world's second largest pool of trained scientists and engineers, integrated into the global intellectual system, to a degree without parallel outside the developed West.

"His legacy is not one we can afford to be complacent about. After all, the roots of Indian science and technology go far deeper than Nehru. The *Rig Veda* asserted that gravitation held the Universe together 24 centuries before the apple fell on Newton's head. The Vedic civilization subscribed to the idea of a spherical earth at a time when everyone else, even the Greeks, assumed the earth was flat. And yet, we lost the global lead in science and technology for over a millennium.

"This New Year's (2007), it is time to resolve that we will never allow ourselves to slip behind again. That will require resources – serious money for research, world-class lab facilities. But above all it will require one commodity India is not short of – brains (and the determination to use them). "Brand IIT" has shown the way. In 2007, we must start to scale this up to the point where one day "Brand India" becomes synonymous not with cheap products or services but with the highest standards of scientific and technological excellence".

No wonder countries in the world, both developing and developed wanting to be global players, are increasingly investing in science as they firmly believe that scientific supremacy is the key to technological innovation and development. Our political decision makers took the right decision after independence, in sharp contrast to our immediate neighbour, to make major investments in institutions dedicated to scientific research and technology development. Our acknowledged strength in nuclear technology, space sciences and satellites launch capabilities, not to mention our global leadership in Information Technology, success of the green revolution and food sufficiency, the white revolution which catapulted India as the world's largest producer of milk and dairy products in the world, etc. are tangible gains of this policy implemented by our visionary leaders of the past. Our initial investments in higher education have paid equally rich dividends – IITs and IIMs are global brand names, with the former ranked at the third position in a recent global ranking.

Information Technology:

Rajiv Gandhi's active years, as the Prime Minister of India, 1984-89, were a period of rapid progress and change. Several new programmes were initiated to create employment and harness science technology, for transforming India into a modern state in the near future. His period witnessed the blossoming of technology more than science.

When Rajiv Gandhi became the Prime Minister of India in 1984, he decided to go ahead with the computerization and in just 15-20 years we became one of the superpowers in software development. This shows how a vision can change the destiny of a nation, practically in no time. His fascination with electronics and telecommunications resulted in revamping the old and antiquated telephone systems to meet public demands. Collaboration with USA, and several European countries brought more investments in R & D in electronics and computer software. During 1985-89, telecommunication was a raging success. It linked remote villages to cities and showed that electronics was not for the benefit of the capitalists alone, but was for the masses as well. He implemented the satellite network programme, linking remote places to the metros. He uplinked India to the global level.

The computer systems, which he introduced, say nearly twenty years ago, have already changed the work culture in the public and private industry as well as in Government administration in the country. What he set in motion still propels every IT professional in India on to greater heights. The mushrooming growth of IT professionals in India and their contributions to the software industry within and outside the country, now stands testimony to his vision of making India proud in the world. He made India a global player in the IT, computer and telecom sectors. Quality of service, rural telephony density, encouraging new technologies for value added services and protecting a reasonable ARPU for telecom service providers will be the key priorities of the Telecom Regulatory Authority of India, by 2007.

Today, the Mobile industry in India has emerged as a shining example – showcasing the success of the reform process. From scarcity, rationing and high tariffs, we have moved to an era of choice, freedom and the lowest tariffs in the world. From a few million phones in the hands of the elite to over 100 million phones in the hands of the common man.. The Indian telecom is celebrating 150 years now, and the Indian market moving towards 300 million customers, with the next generation 3G services and faster growth of broadband and likely migration to NGN (next generation networks) – is a tribute to the visionary Rajiv Gandhi – the architect of the reform process and others who have made it possible, in India.

India is gradually positioning itself to become a global power economically, technologically and politically. The revolution that India is now witnessing *(post – Rajiv Gandhi era)* in information technology, as well as, biotechnology owes much to his dynamism and pioneering efforts- it has changed the face of India, of which we all are beneficiaries today. India has now done it in information technology, pharmaceuticals, and steel and has potential for excelling in new and emerging areas of nanotechnology, pollution and energy saving hybrid cars etc. India is endeavouring to emerge as a knowledge economy in the coming years. The software and IT-enabled services sector is proving to be a major growth engine. Not surprisingly, there is much concern as to whether the sector can keep up a high rate of growth. Current projections of ASSOCHAM 2006 show that growth would sustain in the foreseeable future. There is no doubt that the power of his dreams has resulted in making India – a strong nation marching ahead on the path of progress and prosperity and world peace.

Rajiv Gandhi breathed a new life and a new look for the development and prosperity of India. His youthful energies and dedicated efforts for realizing his vision *India as a prosperous, vibrant and self – reliant nation*, manifested in formulating several path – breaking initiatives, both legislative, administrative and organizational. He was an image booster in every respect for the country. Now his dreams are coming true one by one.

The development of science, technology and society are inter-related and is tightly knit now. Gone are the days when a new scientific idea took ages to give rise to a technological innovation. In turn, a new product emerged slowly to change the culture of the society. It takes place now with breathtaking speed. Indeed technology affects society, as much as society makes choices about technology it wants. We can learn from the symbiosis between technology and society. Witness the love affair of India with Information Technology and cell phones. The coastal landscape has been dramatically changed and the fishermen now get a better prize for their catch, as they can phone / contact the buyers within a second.

Though the Indian society is doing well now, yet the gap between the rich and the poor is still there and need to be bridged. India, known for its software prowess, is increasingly recognized for its strength in pharmaceuticals, manufacturing and automobile components. Its performance in space and nuclear fields attest a newfound confidence.

Rajiv Gandhi laid the foundation for technological progress and today India is getting rich dividends from the initiatives he took. He provided new directions to the development of science and technology for the growth of modern India of the 21st century. He made India a super power in the fields of computer, biotechnology, and human resource development. The dawn of the new millennium is a time to realize ambitious goals. Today, if India is in a position to face the new millennium with newfound confidence, it is solely due to the sagacity and inspiring vision of his dynamic leadership.

Rajiv Gandhi said – As we look towards the next century, when we think of how India is to develop, when we think of new technologies, new science for India, our attention must remain centered on the agricultural sector. This will be so for many years. We have to see how we can develop agriculture; to break the hold of poverty. As India poised itself into the 21st century, with an eight percent growth and a booming industry and export sector, agriculture continues to be the soft under belly. Its growth has been stunted. Employment – particularly of women has grown and the urban-rural divide as wider. Agricultural growth must be accelerated. The information age has made India an emerging economic giant. As we move from an information – based society to a knowledge – based society, we will see India emerging as an even greater power. Today, when the resurgent India marching towards the 21st century, the dream of the architect of modern India of Rajiv Gandhi of giving equal opportunities and benefits of modern technology, to all strata of the society comes true. The visionary inspires us to better the society.

Rajiv Gandhi gave a new direction of thinking, a new strategy and new approach of managing the vast human, as well as, national resources. He gave to the nation a new hope for developing more confidence to become active partner in global progress. India is on the fast track to economic growth with an annual growth rate of 8 per cent well within reach. The prosperity of the 250 million middle class is highly visible, along with those of the poor people.

Dr. Manmohan Singh, Prime Minister of India said in his address to the nation, on 15th August 2004, that – "... Nearly twenty years ago, Rajiv Gandhi first drew the nation's attention to the newly emerging electronics and computer revolution then underway. The enthusiastic manner in which the young people of our country participated in the information technology revolution, turning India into an "IT Superpower" is a tribute to the foresightedness of Rajiv ji."

> Mrs. Sonia Gandhi, said at the naming of the Rajiv Gandhi International Airport, Hyderabad, on 16 March 2005, that – *"Rajiv Gandhi was a leader of the youth who dreamt of a new India and worked towards fulfilling that dream. He lived for the country and gave up his life for the country .... We can see the impression left behind by him on so many works of progress".* The presence of his absence is felt everywhere.

Now, the Indian enterprise is finally finding its own momentum. There are huge problems of poverty and deprivation, but if the country is able to sustain and renew its institutions of democracy and is able to ensure that the fruits of economic progress are widely shared and distributed, India should be able to claim its rightful place in the world economy, proportionate to the size of its population. In terms of absolute size, India could certainly become an economic superpower ..., Rajiv Gandhi gave us a solid foundation to which our economy is booming today. India, a developing country, with fast industrialization and rapid progress on all fronts is making big strides towards global recognition. Apart from the need to accelerate growth and add to output, we have also to deal with what is popularly called the Third wave. To quote a recent commentator: "A wave of technology is crashing upon us that will leave no business, no family, no industry, no institution untouched. Micro – electronics, genetic engineering, artificial intelligence, computer networks – These will change society beyond imagination during the lifetime of most of us".

Prime Minister Dr Manmohan singh, while inaugurating the 52nd Meeting of the National Development Council, NDC, on 9 December 2006, said that the Eleventh Five Year Plan must give priority to redressing the weaknesses in the agricultural sector. Calling for revitalising the sector, he said, "We cannot expect inclusive growth if do not revitalise agriculture. It is important to recognise that the problem is not confined to distribution, with affluent farmers doing well and the small farmers and the landless facing the hardship. Though the weaker groups face more difficulties and need special attention, agriculture as a whole is in the midst of crises. We should focus on achieving higher productivity and incomes for all farmers in both crop and non-crop agriculture." He stressed upon the need to devise plans to uplift the weaker section of the society. The NDC approved the approach paper for the Eleventh Plan, 2007 – 2012, for giving top priority to agriculture, and seeking an ambitious nine percent annual growth.

Our population comprises an overwhelming majority of youth below the age of 25 years. This feature coupled with our deep rooted education system with early focus on mathematics and science, which are perhaps unique to our country, will play a crucial role in our vision of India as a future global power. [1] Rajiv Gandhi had his vision of the modern world *"winged on fast developing technology"*. He considered technology as a major input of economic development and change. And, technology will continue to trigger a faster change in India. This is Rajiv Gandhi's unique contribution to techno-economic development of India. This is his legacy, which the nation will cherish for a long time to come.

Impact of Globalization:

Globalization has also played an important role in bringing in global talent which is why, we see a large number of expatriates wanting to work in India. It is in obvious, there is no looking back for them. India is where the action is. They would rather be a part of it then watch from miles away.

Expert say, it also has to do with the growing economy. After IT, the health care sector is now poised for a big leap. Medical tourism, is now, gaining momentum in India. Recently, even some of the eminent foreign doctors, specialists have shown great interst in serving the poor patients from India and abroad, at affordable cost. Even the USA is considering to import heavy water from India, for its growing nuclear research programme Satellite blast to new high: almost two months after India's space programme took a sky rocketing leap with the Polar Satellite Launch Vehicle(PSLV) flight, it blasted off into higher orbit early on Monday (March 12, 2007) with the successful launch of the indiginious Insat-4-B communication satellite from the kourou in french guiana. At 3,025 Kg, Insat-4 B is one of the heaviest Indain satellites. Its primary role would be to angment direct to home (DTH) TV programmes and also boost their communication services. Developed at a cost of about Rs 210 crores, the satellite is expected to fetch revenue of Rs. 1,250 crores, through DTH.

In a first, India to launch a foreign satellite in April 2007. The 360 Kg. Italian satellite "Agile" will carry out astronomical studies. A foreign satellite will be the main passenger in our recket, and one of our experiment will be piggy-backing on it. This is the first time that the roles have been reversed. For Indian space Programme, the april 2007 flight will be a historical one.

India Poised For Growth -

Visionaries like Pandit Nehru, Indira Gandhi and Rajiv Gandhi, in the past have shaped the destiny of India. For more than ....India, a land of many cultures and many languages. It throws up as many questions as it throws up answers. As India gets more globalised – and may be more complex, people are constantly seeking new answers. How much has the country progressed? How well is the economy doing? For more than half a century, our nation has sprung, stumbled, run fallen, rolled over, got up, dusted herself and cantered, sometimes lurched on. But today, as we begin our 60th year as a free nation, the ride has brought us to the edge of time's great precipice. An India whose faith in success is far greater than its fear of failure. An India that no longer boycotts foreign-made goods but buys out the companies that make them instead. And quietly, while the world is not looking, a pulsating, dynamic, a new India is emerging we all know India has changed dramatically in recent years – there is visible evidence of change all around from the variety of makes of cars on the roads to the number of channels on television set, not to mention infrastructural development, boom in education sector etc. There is transformation of attitude of the Indians. Today there is visibility of the thrilling face of a brave new India.

Dr. A. P. J. Abdul Kalam, President of India, on the occasion of the Republic Day, 26 January 2007, stressed the need to empower all citizens and provide them a good quality of life. He outlined his vision of transforming India into a developed nation before the year 2020, and suggested how different sections of the society can accelerate the process of bringing prosperity to a billion Indians. He further said that – ....Indian economy is in an ascent phase. There is considerable growth in the manufacturing and services sectors. Still a majority of our population who are living in the rural sector have not realized the benefits of the economic growth. Nearly 220 million people are still below poverty line in both rural and urban areas. Even though the GDP growth indicates our economic growth, people's participation is essential for achieving the required targets, focusing the growth of the national prosperity index. It is essential to ensure that all the citizens are empowered with good quality of life encompassing nutritious food, good habitat, good habitat, clean environment, affordable healthcare, quality education with value system and productive employment leading to the comprehensive development of the nation that will bring smiles to one billion people.

"These are indicators for the growth of the National Prosperity Index. To achieve this, we have a vision of transforming India into a developed nation before the year 2020, energizing and igniting the minds of all Indians.

"Every constituent of the government system and corporate sector and the citizens of the nation have to contribute for realizing the mission of Developed India. I would like to suggest the possible contribution from different sections of the society to accelerate the realization of developed India.

"The strength of a billion people who can cohesively become one India in the midst of diversity ahs been the core competence of our nation.

"Capacity to integrate society with technology, knowledge and skills imbibed with our value system derived from our heritage and seamlessly glueing together one billion people in the development process will enhance the national prosperity Index of the nation. Thus, India will have the economic opportunities of the urban areas and the tranquility of life of the rural areas available in both places with high prosperity index. The Indian experience of interconnecting its 600,000 villages to the rest of the country and providing prosperity and equity to one sixth of the population of the planet will serve as a role model for the entire world."

Finally,-

Modern India seen in the right way, is among the world's more scientific countries. Indian scientists see themselves as part of the global enterprise of science.

Rajiv Gandhi did not live on to see his India of the 21st century. But his India lives on to see his dreams. With scientific bent of mind and democratic philosophical attitude, his presence in the 21st century would have definitely made a big difference to this world. His vibrant force of change, brought nearly twenty years ago, still, continues to nurture, shelter, illuminate, enrich and empowers millions of lives today. He was the pride of India. The future beckons India to be prosperous.

References

1. *Rajiv Gandhi – Foundation Day Celebrations, CSIR, 26 September 1987.*
2. *Shashi Tharoor – Looking to the Future with Brand IIT, The Times of India, 31 December 2006.*

3. *Guest Editorial – Current Science, V 91 N 11, p 1435 – 36, 10 December 2006.*
4. *Guest Editorial, Current Science V 91 N 9, 10 November 2006*
5. *ASSOCHAM Study on Business Transformation Outsourcing (BTO) : Third Generation Outsourcing , 2006. New Delhi.*
6. *Swaminathan S Ankelesaria Aiyar- India as a Managerial Number One, The Times of India.31 December 2006*
7. *India Poised – Our Time is Now, The Times of India, 1st January 2007.*
8. *APJ Abdul Kalam – Empowering a Billion Indians. The Times of India, p 2, 26 January 2007.*

India v/s India

There are two Indias in this country.

One India is straining at the leash, eager to spring forth and live up to all the adjectives that the world has been showering recently upon us.

The other India is the leash.

One India says, give me a chance and I will prove myself. The other India says, prove yourself first and maybe then you'll have a chance.

One India lives in the optimism of our hearts. The other India lurks In the skepticism of our minds.

One India wants. The other India hopes.

One India leads. The other India follows.

But conversions are on the rise. With each passing day more and more people from the other India have been coming over to this side.

And quietly, while the world is not looking, a pulsating, dynamic, new India is emerging.

An India whose faith in success is far greater than its fear of failure. An India that no longer boycotts foreign-made goods but buys out the companies that make them instead.

History, they say, is a bad motorist. It rarely ever signals its intentions when it is taking a turn.

This is that rarely-ever moment. History is turning a page.

For more than half a century, our nation has sprung, stumbled, run fallen, rolled over, got up, dusted herself and cantered, sometimes lurched on. But today, as we begin our 60th year as a free nation, the ride has brought us to the edge of time's great precipice.

And one India – a tiny little voice at the back of the head – is looking down at the bottom of the ravine and hesitating.

The other India is looking up at the sky and saying, it's time to fly.

INDIA POISED — our time is now.

* India Poised is an idea that lives within each of us. The anthem is included here in this book, for the sake of future record and refernce purposes.

[Rajiv Gandhi was a catalyst of change, of progress and prosperity of India of 21st century. The transformation of India is due to the dreams of the visionary Rajiv Gandhi.

---

* Courtesy - India Poised, - our time is now, The Times of India, 1st January 2007.

Bibliography

(A) Basic Document

Rajiv Gandhi –

Selected Speeches and Writings of : Vol. I-V (1984-89), Publications Division, Ministry of Information and Broadcasting, Government of India, New Delhi. 1987 – 1989.

Sikka Pawan– Rajiv Gandhii : Selected Speeches on Science and Technology, Uppal Publishing House, Delhi, 2007.

(B) Books, Journals, Newspapers, Articles etc.

Adiraju Venkateser Rao – Gandhi to Gandhi, See Sathya Publications, Hyderabad, 1986.

Aggarwl Adish- Rajiv Gandhi ; An Assessment, Amish Publications, New Delhi, 1993.

Ahluwalia B. K. and Ahluwalia S. – Rajiv Gandhi: Breaking New Grounds, Cosmo Publications, New Delhi, 1985.

Ahluwalia B. K. and Ahluwalia Shashi – Rajiv Gandhi: A Profile in Courage, International Publishing House, New Delhi 1985.

Aluwalia Shashi and Ahluwalia Meenakshi – Assassination of Rajiv Gandhi ,Mittal Publications, New Delhi, 1991.

Aiyar Mani Shankar – Remembering Rajiv, Rupa & Co., New Delhi, 1992.

Aiyar Mani Shankar – In Rajiv's Footprints, Konark Publishers Pvt. Ltd., Delhi, 1993.

Aiyar Swaminathan S. Ankalesaria – India as Managerial Number One, The Times of India, 31 December 2006.

ASSOCHAM Study on Business Transformation Outsourcing (BTO), Third Generation Outsourcing, (ASSOCHAM, New Delhi), 2006.

Bahadur K. P. – Rajiv Gandhi : Man with Destiny, Ess Ess Publications, New Delhi, 1985.

Bedi P. S. and Sharma Roy – Rajiv Gandhi : Our National Hero, Rajindra Publishers and Distributors, Jallandhar (India), 1985.

Bhattacharjee – Rajiv Gandhi; Ashish Publishing Home, New Delhi, 1992.

Chanchreek K. L. and Saroj Prasad – Rajiv Gandhi's Assassination: A Blow to Democracy, H. K. Publishers and Distributors, Delhi, 1991.

Chand Attar – Rajiv Gandhi : His Mind and Ideology, Gian Publishing House, New Delhi, 1991.

Chander Harish and Padmini – Rajiv Gandhi : Many Facets, Noida News Pvt. Ltd., Delhi, 1992.

Chander Harish and Padmini (ed) – Rajiv Gandhi : Human Facet, Noida News Pvt. Ltd., Delhi, 1996.

Chakrabarti Mohit – Rajiv Gandhi : A Portrait, India Publishers & Distributors, Delhi, 1998.

Chidambaram P. – He lived Too Dangerously, The Times of India, New Delhi, 26 May, 1991.

Crosette Barbara – We Have To Do Much More, The Times of India, New Delhi, 26 May, 1991.

Current Science, Guest Editorial, 91 (11) 1435-36, 10 Dec. 2006.

Current Science, Guest Editorial, 91 (9), 10 November 2006.

Desai Dinesh N- Rajiv's India, Parijat Prakashan, Bombay 1985.

Dhawan S.K-Day by Day Account of Rajiv Gandhi (1944-1991), Wave Publications, Delhi 1993.

Gandhi Indira on Science, Technology and Self Reliance, Inaugural Addresses, Indian Science Congress Association, Kolkata, 1985.

Gandhi Rajiv – Tributes and Memories, Wheeler publishers, Allahabad, 1992.

Gandhi Sonia – Rajiv, Viking, Penguin Books India (P) Ltd., New Delhi, 1996.

Gill S. S. – The Dynasty, HarperCollins Publishers India, New Delhi, 1996.

Goenka Shyam-Eternal Rajiv : Epitome of Humanity, Resurgent Publications Pvt. Ltd, New Delhi 2006.

Gupta M.G– Rajiv Gandhi's Foreign Policy. M.G. Publishers, Agra, 1987.

Gupta M.G–The Prime Ministers of India : J.L. Nehru to Rajiv Gandhi, M.G. Publishers and Distributors, Agra, 1986.

Gupta Praney– Venegence : India After the Assassination of Indira Gandhi, W.W. Norton & Co. New York, 1985.

Healy Kathleen – Rajiv Gandhi: The Years of Power, Vikas Publishing House Pvt. Ltd., 1989.

Huda Nurul – The New Choices: Thoughts and Ideas of Rajiv Gandhi, Commonwealth Publishers, New Delhi, 1989.

India Poised – Our Time is Now, The Times of India, 1st January, 2007.

Jain C. K. (ed) – Rajiv Gandhi and Parliament, CBS Publishers and Distributors, New Delhi, 1992.

Jarg M. S. – From the Heights of Flying to the Heights of Fame, V. K. Enterprise, New Delhi, 1986.

Kalam, APJ-Empowering a Billion Indians, The Times of India, New Delhi, 26 January 2007.

Khoshoo T. N. – Indira Gandhi on Science, Technology and Self-Reliance, ISCA, Kolkata, 1985.

Karthikeyan D. R. and Radha Vinod Raju – Triumph of Truth: The Rajiv Gandhi's Assassinatation, New Dawn Press Inc., New Delhi, 2004.

Merchant Mirihaz – Rajiv Gandhi: The End of a Dream, Viking, Penguin, New Delhi, 1991.

Mittal Rajeev – Rajiv Gandhi: The Theme of Today, Shakuntla Foundations, Chandigarh, 1981.

Murthy V. K. and Sharma Gautam – Rajiv Gandhi: Challenges and Choices, Radiant Publishers, New Delhi, 1986.

National Herald – Remembering Rajiv: A Tribute, 21 May, 1992.

National Herald: Special Number on Rajiv Gandhi, In Memoriam, New Delhi, 1993.

Nehru Jawahar Lal – Speeches Vol. III; Ministry of Information and Broadcasting, Govt. of India, New Delhi, 1958.

Nehru Jawahar Lal – The Discovery of India, Meridian Books Limited, London, 1951.

Nugent Nicholas – Rajiv Gandhi: Son of a Dynasty. BBC Books, London, 1990.

Perspective in Science and Technology, - Recommendations of SAC-PM, Vikas Publishing House, New Delhi 1990.

Prime Minister Rajiv Gandhi"s Visits USSR – Soviet Land Booklets, USSR Embassy in India, New Delhi, 1985.

Ponkshe Satyawrat – Rajiv Gandhi: The Pragmatic Prime Minister of India, Bhate and Ponkshe Publications, Pune, 1986.

Pradhan R. D. – Working with Rajiv Gandhi, Indus, HarperCollins Publishers, India, New Delhi, 1995.

Raju Jagmohan Singh – Quotes of Rajiv Gandhi, UBS Publishers & Distributors, New Delhi, 1994.

Rasgotra Maharaj Krishna – Rajiv Gandhi's World View, Vikas Publishing House Pvt. Ltd. New Delhi, 1991.

Roy Sekhar Basu (ed) – The Legacy of Rajiv Gandhi, New Approach, Kolkatta, 2006.

Sengupta Bhabani – Rajiv Gandhi: A Political Study, Konark Publishers Pvt. Ltd., Delhi, 1989.

Shah M. C. – Rajiv Gandhi in Parliament, Shipra, New Delhi, 1991.

Sharma Rajeev – Beyond the Tigers: Tracking Rajiv Gandhi's Assassination, Kaveri Books, New Delhi, 1998.

Sharma Satinder and Sharma Indira – Rajiv Gandhi: An Annotated Bibliography (1944-82), Sawan Publication, Delhi, 1983.

Singh Gobind– Rajiv Gandhi, Sanmarg Prakashan, 1987.

Singh K. Natwar and Sharda Prasad H. Y. – Rajiv Gandhi: A Political Study, Konark Publishers Pvt. Ltd., Delhi, 1989.

Singh Rai – Resurgence of Rajiv Gandhi: ABC Publishing House, New Delhi, 1985.

Singh Ranbir and Khosla M. – Rajiv Gandhi, Emkay Publishers Pvt. Ltd., New Delhi, 1992.

Sood P. – Rajiv Gandhi: The Brave New Leader, Marwah Publications, New Delhi, 1986.

Sikka Pawan – Rajiv Gandhi – Environment, Prime Concern, National Herald, New Delhi, 20 August, 2003.

Sikka Pawan – Rajiv Gandhi: He wanted to see India Proud, National herald, New Delhi, 21 May, 2005.

Sikka Pawan– Rajiv Gandhi : His Vision of 21st Century -Science, Technology and National Development, Kalpaz Publications, Delhi, 2007.

Swamy Subramaniam – The Assassination of Rajiv Gandhi: Unanswered Questions and Unasked Queries, Konark Publishers Pvt. Ltd., Delhi, 2000.

Tharoor Shashi – Looking to the Future with Brand IIT; The Times of India, New Delhi, 31 December, 2006.

Tokas Jagdish Chander – Rajiv Gandhi: Future of India, Pustkayan, New Delhi, 1987.

Varma Umashankar Prasad – Rajiv Gandhi and Morality in Public Affairs, Mittal Publications, Delhi, 1988.

Varma Shrikant – A Portrait of Rajiv Gandhi, Arnold Heinemann, New Delhi, 1985.

Zaidi A. M. – Rajiv Gandhi, Towards Peace, Progress and Prosperity, Indian Institute of Political Research, New Delhi, 1987.

Index